# ORDER FORM FOR PHOTOGRAPHS

To: Ulster Folk & Transport Museum (Department of Photography)
    Cultra, Holywood, Co. Down BT18 0EU, Northern Ireland

*Please supply the following photographs from the HARLAND and WOLFF COLLECTION:*

GW00585914

| REF. NO. | NUMBER OF PRINTS<br>10″ x 8″ (Nominal) @ £3.45 each | NUMBER OF PRIN<br>20″ x 16″ (Nominal) @ £ | |
|---|---|---|---|
| | | | |
| POSTAGE & PACKING (Surface mail — Airmail extra) | | | £1.00 |
| TOTAL REMITTANCE IN STERLING | | | . |

Name . . . . . . . . . . . . . . . . . . . . . . . . . . . . . . . . . . . . . . . . . . . . . . . . . . . . . . . . . . . . . . . .

Address . . . . . . . . . . . . . . . . . . . . . . . . . . . . . . . . . . . . . . . . . . . . . . . . . . . . . . . . . . . . . . .

. . . . . . . . . . . . . . . . . . . . . . . . . . . . . . . . . . . . . . . . . . . . . . . . . . . . . . . . . . . . . . . . . . . . .

**ALLOW 28 DAYS FOR DELIVERY**

# STEEL SHIPS AND IRON MEN

*To the chairman, directors and workforce of Harland and Wolff Holdings PLC*

The publication of this book has been assisted generously
by the Ulster Folk and Transport Museum, Cultra.

The Friar's Bush Press
24 College Park Avenue
Belfast BT7 1LR

Published 1989
© Copyright reserved
ISBN 0 946872 23 6

Designed by Rodney Miller Associates, Belfast
Printed by W. & G. Baird, Antrim

COVER PHOTOGRAPHS

Front Cover: *TITANIC (401) leaving Belfast, 2 April 1912. (H1721)*
Back Cover: *'Black Squad'/CHINA (299). Photograph No. 54 (H396A).*

# STEEL & IRON
## S·H·I·P·S & M·E·N

*Shipbuilding in Belfast, 1894–1912*

*Michael McCaughan*

*The Harland & Wolff Historic Photograph Collection
at the Ulster Folk & Transport Museum*

# The Harland & Wolff
# Historic Photograph Collection

In October 1987 Mr T John Parker, chairman and chief executive of Harland & Wolff plc, formally presented the company's photographic archive to the Ulster Folk & Transport Museum. Comprising some 75,000 negatives, it provides a remarkable visual record of the development and achievements of the world famous shipbuilding firm, from the mid 1890s to almost the present day. This specialist photographic collection is of international significance because it depicts the changing output and infrastructure of a shipbuilding company that has always been, and continues to be, at the leading edge of naval architecture and marine technology.

Drawing on the collection, this book is a visual account of shipbuilding at Queen's Island from 1894 to 1912. It is also intended to encourage public use of the collection, by means of the specially prepared catalogue section which covers the same period and carries reference to over 2,000 negatives. Prints can be ordered from the museum's department of photography, whose head, Mr. T K Anderson, played a key role in securing the archive for the museum. Besides initiating necessary conservation work, including the making of duplicate film negatives of early glass plates, Kenneth Anderson has organised the printing of some 6,500 photographs dating from 1894 onwards. These have been bound and are available for consultation in the Museum Library. The time-consuming and expensive task of printing was made possible by generous sponsorship from Harland & Wolff plc, in conjunction with the

Association for Business Sponsorship of the Arts, and also from Kentmere Ltd, who provided the photographic paper.

## The shipyard and photography

From the beginning of their partnership in 1861, Edward Harland & G W Wolff established a reputation for constructing high quality ships designed to suit an owner's particular requirements. Furthermore, their ships frequently combined advanced technology with innovative naval architecture. For example, during the 1860s, the firm's entirely new concepts in iron ship design provided hull strength and additional cargo capacity without increase in engine size and hence without increase in fuel consumption. After 1880 the company made significant advances in steam engine design and in the twentieth century in diesel and turbo-electric machinery. As shipbuilders with a large output of passenger vessels, they pioneered improvements in the quality of accommodation in all classes, most notably in ships built for the White Star Line. The company also developed the capacity to construct ships of huge dimensions, although in recent years these have been tankers and bulk carriers, rather than passenger liners. Ship repair work continues to be an important part of the company's activities, as does design and build capability in the highly specialised field of naval contracts. Today Harland & Wolff are still at the forefront of sophisticated shipbuilding technology, with the construction of the

BP SWOPS vessel for the exploitation of small offshore oil fields, considered uneconomic to develop by conventional means.

The earliest negatives in the archive relate to ship construction in the mid 1890s, although a few surviving H&W photograph albums contain prints dating to the 1860s and 70s. However, it is only from 1894 onwards that the collection becomes coherent and comprehensive in its range. A particularly important sequence from this period documents progress in building ship No. 317, the giant White Star liner OCEANIC, which when delivered in August 1899 was the largest and most luxurious liner in the world. The detailed photographic record covers keel laying, framing, shell plating, launch and outfitting, including installation of machinery and the completion of passenger accommodation. Of course such coverage was usual only for the most important contracts and vessels of less significance were generally photographed before, during and after launch, then again when completed or nearing completion. Besides photographs of such famous ships as TITANIC, GEORGIC, CAPETOWN CASTLE, ANDES, HMS BELFAST, HMS EAGLE, SOUTHERN CROSS & CANBERRA, the collection includes important evidence of changes in the working life of the shipyard, in way of plant, facilities, offices, workshops, equipment and personnel.

Over the years different photographers have been responsible for maintaining and enhancing the archive, which is characterised by negatives of high quality and content. Photographs were, and of course continue to be, required for a variety of reasons, including the recording of significant events or stages of construction, the documenting of technical detail and the provision of material for marketing and promotional purposes. Prior to the early 1920s, when the company established its own permanent photographic department, the majority of photographs were taken by the well known Belfast professional photographr R J Welch. From the mid 1890s he worked as Harland & Wolff's official photographer and his initials appear on virtually every glass plate from 1894 to the First World War. Welch's photographs form an outstanding record of shipyard plant and production during this period. Often taken in the most difficult of circumstances, these photographs, with their great depth of field and carefully selected viewpoints, are models of industrial photography. They set high standards for later photographers working with more sophisticated equipment and materials. Welch shared Harland & Wolff's pride in the extensive shipbuilding enterprise at Queen's Island and was determined to make his photographs 'the best possible record for the benefit of future generations.' Essentially it is to the overriding Victorian desire to provide visual evidence of industrial progress and achievement that the Harland & Wolff photographic archive owes its origins.

MICHAEL McCAUGHAN
ULSTER FOLK AND TRANSPORT MUSEUM

# Works and Design

Shipyard men swarm down Queen's Road at the end of a working day in May 1911. Many of them are boarding trams for parts of the city beyond walking distance. At this period about 14,000 men were employed by Harland & Wolff at Queen's Island. (H1555).

*When completed in 1911 and 1912 OLYMPIC (400) and TITANIC (401) were the largest ships in the world. Their construction represented the peak of shipbuilding achievement at Belfast prior to the First World War. In March 1912 the two sisterships were together for the last time, when OLYMPIC returned to Belfast for drydocking and TITANIC was nearing completion at the Thompson deepwater wharf. (H1637).*

*Private office of Harland & Wolff's chairman, Lord Pirrie, c.1912. Pictures on the wall include framed photographs of the company's founders, Edward Harland (right) and G W Wolff (left). The stained glass window over the fireplace was presented to the museum in 1989 and is now on display in the Witham Street Transport Gallery, close to the shipyard in East Belfast. (H503).*

*Naval architects engaged in ship design in the hull drawing office c.1912.*
*The high barrel ceiling and the large number of windows make maximum*
*use of natural light. (H501).*

*Interior of the generating station which provided electrical power for tools and lighting throughout the shipyard, June 1912. The station was commissioned on 24 October 1904, when the supply of current from Belfast Corporation ceased. (H614).*

*Mould loft c.1910 with three loftsmen chalking the lines of a ship on portable wooden flooring, full size for cross section and quarter scale for length, in order to determine the precise shapes of required hull frames. The floor to ceiling windows maximise natural light, whilst the Belfast truss roof combines a large span with relatively low weight. (H57).*

# Construction

*Hydraulic riveting of keel and vertical keel plate, or centre plate, of oil tanker IROQUOIS (385) on No. 2 slip North Yard, c.May 1906. This is the spinal column of the vessel and it rests on wooden keel blocks carefully aligned at the correct inclination for a smooth launch. (H1064).*

8

*Erected stern frames of OCEANIC (317) on No. 2 slip North Yard, 3
November 1897. When completed the complex arrangement of connected
steel hull frames becomes a skeletal structure of immense strength. (H38).*

*Shell plating ADRIATIC (358) on No. 3 slip North Yard, c.March 1906.*
*Heavy timber shores have been erected by shipwrights to keep the steel*
*structure in place until all the shell plates have been riveted together and*
*to the frames, while the arrangement of wooden staging allows riveters*
*to work on the hull. (H976).*

*The huge Arrol gantry was erected to permit the building of OLYMPIC (400) and TITANIC (401) on North Yard reconstructed slips 2 and 3. The light grey painted hull of OLYMPIC is being prepared for launch, while on No. 3 slip, shell plating of TITANIC has been completed, October 1910. (H1440).*

*Turning a main crankshaft journal in the Engine Works for the propelling machinery of OCEANIC (317), 1 October 1898. When completed, the ship's two sets of reciprocating engines were the largest in the world. (H165).*

*Boilers for OCEANIC (317) under construction in the Boiler Shop, November 1898. (H175).*

*Internal construction of ADRIATIC (358) with men working on the coamings of a hatchway, c.March 1906. The 'Islandmen' had diverse hobbies and one of this group, Robert Bell, was an amateur geologist and mineralist who had several species of fossil mollusca named after him. (H978).*

*Men fitting the starboard tail shaft of TITANIC (401) a few weeks before launching on 31 May 1911. The propellers were not fitted until the ship was drydocked in February 1912. This unusual photograph demonstrates the huge size of TITANIC and clearly shows the arrangement of riveted shell plating around the sternpost. It also suggests the dangers of shipyard work and practice. (H1557).*

15

# Launch

ADRIATIC (358) prepared for launch from No. 3 slip North Yard on 20 September 1906. The anchor chains looped along the sides of the hull are part of the arrangement of drag chains to arrest the momentum of the ship in the water. The stern floats first and as it rises up, enormous pressure is taken by the timber cradle which supports the bows still sliding down the ways. ADRIATIC's launch weight of 14,910 tons was the shipyard's largest up to this date. The steel stockyard in the foreground has plates stacked vertically for ease of handling. (H989).

*Launch party on platform immediately before the naming ceremony of WALMER CASTLE (342) on 6 July 1901. W J Pirrie is third from the right and standing next to him is Sir Donald Currie, chairman of the Union-Castle Line. G W Wolff is fifth from the left, wearing a white hat. (H712).*

*Launch of NIEUW AMSTERDAM (366) from No. 1 slip North Yard, 28 September 1905. A ship sliding down the greased ways to her natural element is always a dramatic event in the work of a shipyard. Within a few seconds an inert structure of steel becomes a floating vessel and so the launch is an occasion on which feelings of relief and achievement are tinged with poignancy. (H967).*

18

*Launch of BRITON (313) from old No. 9 slip, renumbered 4, North Yard,*
*5 June 1897. The anchor chains are straining to arrest the momentum of*
*the 5671 ton hull moving through the water. (H89).*

*The largest ship of the nineteenth century OCEANIC (317) floats high in the water immediately after her launch on 14 January 1899. Men in pulling boats are beginning to recover small pieces of launch debris and a paddle tug is manoeuvring to bring OCEANIC round to the fitting-out wharf for completion. (H252).*

*When launched from No. 2 slip North Yard on 4 April 1901, CELTIC (335) was the largest ship in the world. Men on the slip are beginning to clear the ways, which have been lubricated with tallow and soft soap, in preparation for laying the keel of the next ship. On the water men in a scow recover launch debris while tugs prepare to manoeuvre CELTIC to her fitting-out wharf. (H698).*

# Fitting Out

*Shipyard workers disembarking from OLYMPIC (400) in the final weeks of fitting out, at the Thompson deepwater wharf, May 1911. The 200 ton floating crane is positioned between the ship and the wharf to enable heavy equipment to be lifted on board. Between 3000 and 4000 men were engaged on the completion of OLYMPIC, both on board and in the shops. (H1516A).*

*OLYMPIC (400) was the first ship to enter the new Thompson (Era) Graving Dock on 1 April 1911 for necessary completion work, including the fitting of her three huge propellers. (H1511).*

*15½ ton anchor, on a wagon drawn by seven horses, outside the main offices on Queen's Road en route to OLYMPIC (400), October 1910. (H1449).*

*Funnel section on a tramway wagon, brought to Alexandra Wharf for lifting on board OCEANIC (317), fitting out alongside, March 1899. (H261).*

*Installing boilers in stokehold of OCEANIC (317) during outfitting, February 1899. The ship was equipped with twelve double-ended and three single-ended coal-fired boilers supplying steam at a working pressure of 192 p.s.i. (H256).*

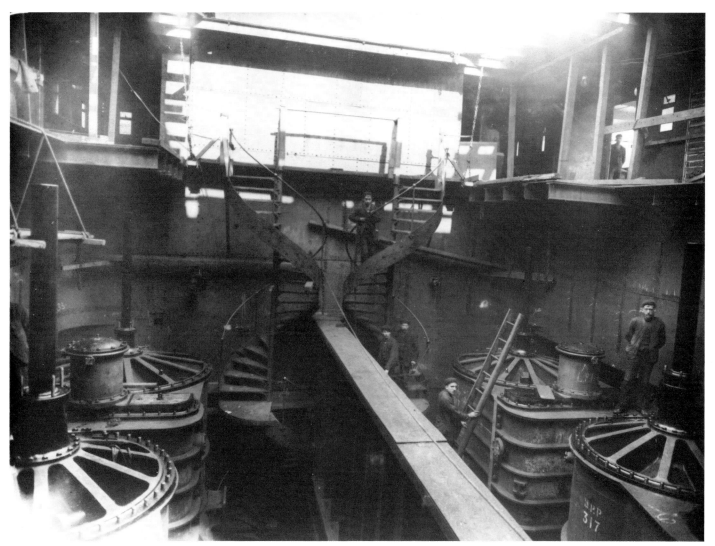

*Installing port and starboard main engines of OCEANIC (317) during outfitting, March 1899. The two sets of 4-cylinder triple expansion engines are separated by a fore and aft bulkhead. (H262).*

*Painters working on embossed panels in the painters' studio for the interior decoration of a passenger ship, 1899. (H505).*

*The passenger accommodation of the White Star Line's OCEANIC (317) was intended to be the most luxurious and spectacular on the North Atlantic. The architect Richard Norman Shaw acted as consultant for much of the interior design, including the dome and richly decorated panels of the first class dining saloon. The specialist contractor G Trollope & Sons undertook the work in the saloon, which was nearing completion on 1 June 1899. (H278).*

# Completion

*SAXON (326) was built for the Union Line's South African service and delivered in June 1900. (H662).*

*First class library and writing room of SAXON (326), June 1900 (H651).*

*Adjusting the standard compass of the Dominion Line's NEW ENGLAND (315) during her trial trip, June 1898. It was Harland & Wolff's practice for a new ship to be taken down Belfast Lough by her own crew, assisted by shipyard men and others, such as the compass specialist. (H215).*

*First class dining saloon of the North Atlantic liner NEW ENGLAND (315), June 1898. (H223).*

*Third class dining saloon of GASCON (304), completed in February 1897
for the Union Line's South African service. (H81).*

*Third class dining saloon of PERICLES (392), completed in June 1908 for the Aberdeen Line's Australian service. Unusually the tables have been laid for the photograph. (H1260).*

*MINNEAPOLIS (328) was built for the Atlantic Transport Company's London–New York service and was completed in March 1900. Extensive first class accommodation was combined with very large cargo capacity. (H436).*

*Master and officers on the bridge of MINNEHAHA (329), sistership of
MINNEAPOLIS (328), at sea in Belfast Lough, July 1900. (H449).*

*Completed stokehold of Royal Mail's ARAGON (367), June 1905. Three double-ended and three single-ended coal-fired boilers supplied steam to two quadruple expansion engines at a working pressure of 215 p.s.i. (H899).*

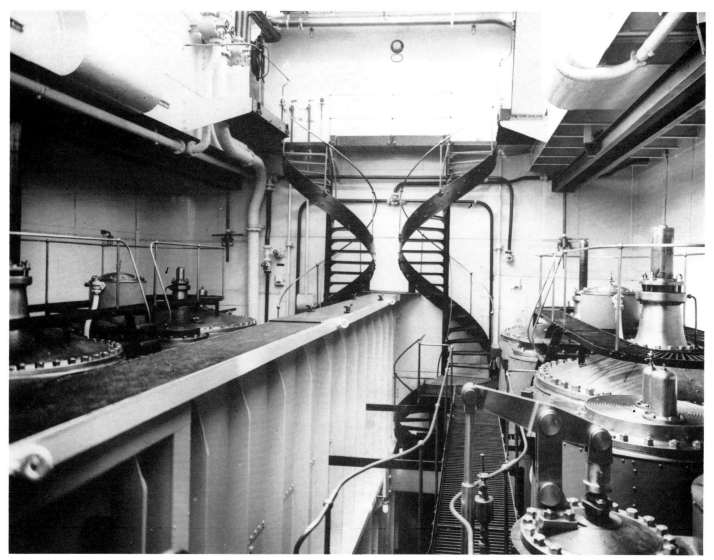

*Cylinder heads of port and starboard engines in completed engine room
of OCEANIC (317), August 1899. (H336).*

*Completed and working galley of Royal Mail's AMAZON (372), sistership of ARAGON (367), June 1906. (H1068).*

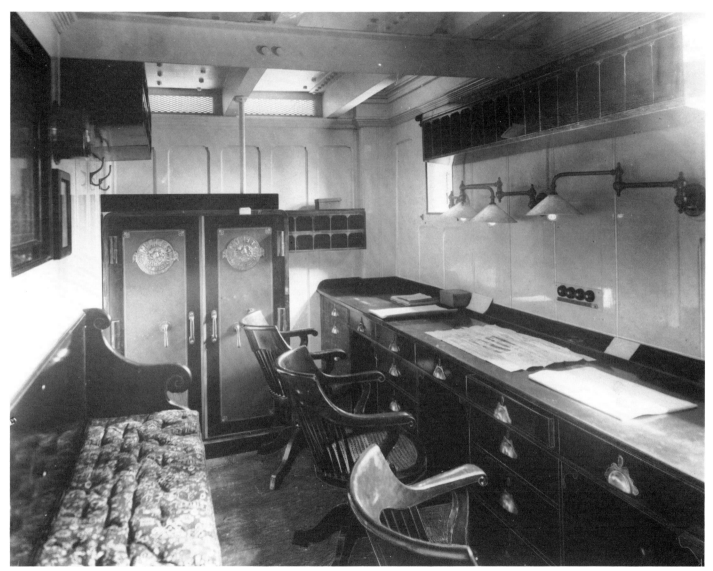

*Purser's office, complete with safe, ARAGON (367), June 1905. (H927).*

*STATENDAM (320) being manoeuvred into drydock before final handover
to the Holland-America Line, August 1898. (H220).*

*Shipyard workers viewing LAURENTIC (394) in Belfast Lough from the stern of a tug, April 1909. Built for White Star's Canadian service, she was the first vessel to be fitted with triple screws driven by a combination of twin reciprocating engines and a low pressure turbine. (H1349).*

*Third class general room of SUEVIC (333), completed in March 1901 for White Star's newly opened passenger and cargo service between Liverpool and Australia, via the Cape. The ship was designed to carry over 400 passengers, mainly emigrants, and all third class. Note the piano on the left and the mast on the right. (H682).*

*First class social hall and music gallery of ARAGON (367), completed in June 1905 for Royal Mail's Southampton—Brazil—River Plate service. She was the first of a series of Royal Mail ships famous for their elegance and luxury. The inclusion of the five uniformed musicians in the photograph is most unusual and indicative of the importance of the vessel. (H941).*

*Advanced passenger ships were designed with innovative facilities, such as the barber's shop in ARAGON (367), June 1905. (H906).*

For the recreation of health conscious first class passengers, White Star's
*TITANIC* (401) had a fully equipped gymnasium, March 1912. Mr. T
W McCauley, the physical educator, remained at his post on the fateful
night of 14/15 April 1912 and went down with the ship. (H1730).

*Third class twenty-berth cabin on MEDIC (323), completed in July 1899*
*for White Star's Australian service. Besides cargo, the ship could carry*
*about 350 single class passengers, mainly emigrants, who travelled at very*
*low rates. (H389).*

*Second class four-berth cabin on ROTTERDAM (390), completed in June 1908 for the Holland-America Line's service between Rotterdam and New York. Accommodation on passenger liners was often described as first for luxury, second for comfort and third for economy. (H1307).*

Bedroom of first class suite B60 on bridge deck of TITANIC (401), March 1912. Built for White Star's Southampton–New York service, TITANIC and her sistership OLYMPIC (400) introduced new standards of accommodation in all three classes. First class was the embodiment of luxury and elegance at sea. White Star grandiloquently and ironically claimed that . . . 'the staterooms in their situation, spaciousness and appointments, will be perfect havens of retreat where many pleasant hours are spent, and where the time given to slumber and rest will be free from noise or other disturbance.' (H1726).

*Final view of TITANIC (401) in Belfast Lough, 2 April 1912. The Belfast News Letter reported that . . . 'The mammoth vessel presented an impressive and picturesque spectacle, looking perfect from keel to truck, while the weather conditions were happily of a favourable character. When the tugs were left behind the compasses were adjusted, after which a satisfactory speed run took place, and the latest triumph of the ship builder's art then left for Southampton, carrying with her the best wishes of the citizens of Belfast.' (H1723).*

# Repairs
# and
# Refitting

Ship repair and refitting has been an important part of Harland & Wolff's business from the early years of the company. Often this work requires considerable ingenuity and engineering skill, as in the 1897 operation to lengthen the Hamburg-Amerika liner AUGUSTA VICTORIA, by inserting a new length of hull amidships. (H67).

*When the White Star liner SUEVIC (333, 1901) ran aground on rocks near the Lizard in March 1907 , it proved impossible to refloat the ship as a whole, so the undamaged stern half was cut away and taken to Southampton. To effect repairs a complete new bow section was built in Belfast, launched on 5 October 1907 and towed to Southampton where the two parts of the hull were joined together. (H1175).*

*The 'black squad,' who undertook particularly hard and dirty work, pose under the damaged hull of the P.&O. liner CHINA (299, 1896) in Alexandra Graving Dock. The ship had been salvaged and brought back to Belfast for repairs after running ashore on the Red Sea island of Perim in March 1898. (H396A).*

*The P.&O. liner CHINA (299, 1896) in Belfast Lough after extensive repairs and refitting, 1899. The complete rebuilding of the bow and much of the bottom of the ship, following a six month salvage operation, was a remarkable engineering achievement by Harland & Wolff. (H424).*

**ALPHABETICAL LIST OF SHIPS,** WHICH IN THE CATALOGUE ARE ARRANGED CHRONOLOGICALLY BY THE H&W SHIP NUMBER. THE CATALOGUE COMPRISES ALL SURVIVING H&W GLASS PLATE NEGATIVES OF SHIPS COMPLETED TO 31 DECEMBER 1912 AND VIEWS OF THE SHIPYARD TO THE SAME DATE.

| NAME | SHIP NO. | COMPLETED |
|---|---|---|
| ABOSSO | 430 | 1912 |
| ADRIATIC | 358 | 1907 |
| AFRIC | 322 | 1899 |
| AMAZON | 372 | 1906 |
| AMERIKA | 357 | 1905 |
| ARABIC (MINNEWASKA) | 340 | 1903 |
| ARAGON | 367 | 1905 |
| ARLANZA | 415 | 1912 |
| ASTURIAS | 388 | 1908 |
| ATHENIC | 341 | 1902 |
| ATLANTIC | 74 | 1871 |
| AVON | 382 | 1907 |
| BALANTIA | 406 | 1909 |
| BALTIC | 75 | 1871 |
| BALTIC | 352 | 1904 |
| BERBICE | 405 | 1909 |
| BRITANNIC | 83 | 1874 |
| BRITON | 313 | 1897 |
| CANADA | 300 | 1896 |
| CEDRIC | 337 | 1903 |
| CELTIC | 335 | 1901 |
| CESTRIAN | 296 | 1896 |
| CEVIC | 270 | 1894 |
| CHINA | 299 | 1896 |
| COLUMBUS (REPUBLIC) | 345 | 1903 |
| COMMONWEALTH | 330 | 1900 |
| CUFIC | 210 | 1888 |
| CYMRIC | 316 | 1898 |
| DARRO | 427 | 1912 |
| DEMOSTHENES | 418 | 1911 |
| DERBYSHIRE | 314 | 1897 |
| DESEADO | 420 | 1912 |
| DUNLUCE CASTLE | 361 | 1904 |
| EDINBURGH CASTLE | 410 | 1910 |
| ENCHANTRESS, HMS | 360 | 1904 |
| GALEKA | 347 | 1899 |
| GALWAY CASTLE | 419 | 1911 |
| GASCON | 304 | 1897 |
| GEORGIC | 293 | 1895 |
| GERMAN | 334 | 1898 |
| GERMANIC | 85 | 1875 |
| GLOUCESTERSHIRE | 411 | 1910 |
| GOORKHA | 311 | 1897 |
| GOTHIC (GOTHLAND) | 267 | 1893 |
| GUELPH | 284 | 1894 |
| IROQUOIS | 385 | 1907 |
| KAROOLA | 404 | 1909 |
| KENILWORTH CASTLE | 356 | 1904 |
| LAPLAND | 393 | 1909 |
| LAURENTIC (ALBERTA) | 394 | 1909 |
| LEICESTERSHIRE | 403 | 1909 |
| MAJESTIC | 209 | 1890 |
| MALOJA | 414 | 1911 |
| MALLINA | 407 | 1909 |
| MARMORA | 350 | 1903 |
| MEDIC | 323 | 1899 |
| MEGANTIC | 399 | 1909 |
| MINNEAPOLIS | 328 | 1900 |
| MINNEHAHA | 329 | 1900 |
| MINNETONKA | 339 | 1902 |
| MINNEWASKA | 397 | 1909 |
| NAVAHOE | 389 | 1908 |
| NEW ENGLAND | 315 | 1898 |
| NIEUW AMSTERDAM | 366 | 1906 |
| NOMADIC | 422 | 1911 |
| NORMAN | 280 | 1894 |
| OCEANIC | 73 | 1871 |
| OCEANIC | 317 | 1899 |
| OLYMPIC | 400 | 1911 |
| ORONSA | 377 | 1906 |
| OXFORDSHIRE | 429 | 1912 |
| PAKEHA | 409 | 1910 |
| PARDO | 363 | 1904 |
| PATRIOTIC | 424 | 1912 |
| PENNSYLVANIA | 302 | 1897 |
| PERICLES | 392 | 1908 |
| PERSIC | 325 | 1899 |
| POTARO | 364 | 1904 |
| PRESIDENT LINCOLN (SERVIAN) | 353 | 1907 |
| REPUBLIC | 76 | 1872 |
| ROTTERDAM | 312 | 1897 |
| ROTTERDAM | 390 | 1908 |
| RUNIC | 211 | 1889 |
| RUNIC | 332 | 1900 |
| RYNDAM | 336 | 1901 |
| SACHSEN | 413 | 1911 |
| SAXON | 326 | 1900 |
| STATENDAM | 320 | 1898 |
| SUEVIC | 333 | 1901 |
| THEMISTOCLES | 412 | 1911 |
| TITANIC | 401 | 1912 |
| WALMER CASTLE (CELT) | 342 | 1902 |
| WINIFREDIAN | 324 | 1899 |
| ZEALANDIC | 421 | 1911 |

| SHIP NO: 73 | | NAME: OCEANIC |
|---|---|---|
| TYPE: Passenger Ship | TONNAGE: 3808 | LAUNCH: 27 August 1870 |
| DELIVERY: 24 February 1871 | OWNER: Oceanic Steam Navigation Company (White Star Line) | |

| REF. NO. | DATE | MAIN SUBJECT |
|---|---|---|
| H242-243 | c.August 1899 | Office display of half models of White Star liners OCEANIC (73), MAJESTIC (209) and OCEANIC (II, 317). |
| H2331 | | Photograph of a lithograph depicting port profile of OCEANIC/ATLANTIC/BALTIC/REPUBLIC at sea c.1872. |

| SHIP NO: 74 | | NAME: ATLANTIC |
|---|---|---|
| TYPE: Passenger Ship | TONNAGE: 3708 | LAUNCH: 26 November 1870 |
| DELIVERY: 3 June 1871 | OWNER: Oceanic Steam Navigation Company (White Star Line) | |

| REF. NO. | DATE | MAIN SUBJECT |
|---|---|---|
| H2331 | | Photograph of lithograph depicting port profile of OCEANIC/ATLANTIC/BALTIC/REPUBLIC at sea. |

| SHIP NO: 75 | | NAME: BALTIC |
|---|---|---|
| TYPE: Passenger Ship | TONNAGE: 3708 | LAUNCH: 8 March 1871 |
| DELIVERY: 2 September 1871 | OWNER: Oceanic Steam Navigation Company (White Star Line) | |

| REF. NO. | DATE | MAIN SUBJECT |
|---|---|---|
| H2331 | | Photograph of a lithograph depicting port profile of OCEANIC/ATLANTIC/BALTIC/REPUBLIC at sea. |

| SHIP NO: 76 | | NAME: REPUBLIC |
|---|---|---|
| TYPE: Passenger Ship | TONNAGE: 3708 | LAUNCH: 4 July 1871 |
| DELIVERY: 21 January 1872 | OWNER: Oceanic Steam Navigation Company (White Star Line) | |

| REF. NO. | DATE | MAIN SUBJECT |
|---|---|---|
| H2331 | | Photograph of a lithograph depicting port profile of OCEANIC/ATLANTIC/BALTIC/REPUBLIC at sea. |

| SHIP NO: 83 | | NAME: BRITANNIC |
|---|---|---|
| TYPE: Passenger Ship | TONNAGE: 5004 | LAUNCH: 3 February 1874 |
| DELIVERY: 6 June 1874 | OWNER: Oceanic Steam Navigation Company (White Star Line) | |

| REF. NO. | DATE | MAIN SUBJECT |
|---|---|---|
| H770 | c.September 1902 | Starboard bow view, alongside CEDRIC (337) outfitting. |
| H771-771A | c.September 1902 | Starboard profile alongside CEDRIC outfitting. Sold to German breakers 1903. |

| SHIP NO: 85 | | NAME: GERMANIC |
|---|---|---|
| TYPE: Passenger Ship | TONNAGE: 5008 | LAUNCH: 15 July 1874 |
| DELIVERY: 24 April 1875 | OWNER: Oceanic Steam Navigation Company (White Star Line) | |

| REF. NO. | DATE | MAIN SUBJECT |
|---|---|---|
| H2362 | c.1895 | Port bow ¾ profile alongside wharf, Abercorn Basin, after refitting. |

| SHIP NO: 209 | | NAME: MAJESTIC |
|---|---|---|
| **TYPE:** Passenger Ship | **TONNAGE:** 9861 | **LAUNCH:** 29 June 1889 |
| **DELIVERY:** 22 March 1890 | **OWNER:** Oceanic Steam Navigation Company (White Star Line) | |

| REF. NO. | DATE | MAIN SUBJECT |
|---|---|---|
| H242-243 | c.August 1899 | Office display of half models of White Star liners OCEANIC (73), MAJESTIC (209), & OCEANIC (II, 317). |

| SHIP NO: 210/211 | | NAME: CUFIC/RUNIC |
|---|---|---|
| **TYPE:** Livestock Carrier | **TONNAGE:** 4639 | **LAUNCH:** 10 October 1888 1 January 1889 |
| **DELIVERY:** 1 December 1888 16 February 1889 | **OWNER:** Oceanic Steam Navigation Company (White Star Line) | |

| REF. NO. | DATE | MAIN SUBJECT |
|---|---|---|
| H730-731 | August 1901 | Office display of half models of White Star ships CUFIC/RUNIC (210-211), CEVIC (270) & CELTIC (335). |

| SHIP NO: 267 | | NAME: GOTHIC (GOTHLAND 1907–11) |
|---|---|---|
| **TYPE:** Passenger Ship | **TONNAGE:** 7669 | **LAUNCH:** 28 June 1893 |
| **DELIVERY:** 28 November 1893 | **OWNER:** Oceanic Steam Navigation Company (White Star Line) Red Star Line from 1907 | |

| REF. NO. | DATE | MAIN SUBJECT |
|---|---|---|
| H1117 | 1907 | Port stern ¾ profile at Abercorn Basin in Red Star Line livery and renamed GOTHLAND. |
| H1117A&B | 1907 | Starboard bow view under tow after refitting for Red Star and renamed GOTHLAND. |
| H1118 | 1907 | View along upper promenade deck. |
| H1119-1120 | 1907 | Third class dining saloon. |

| SHIP NO: 270 | | NAME: CEVIC |
|---|---|---|
| **TYPE:** Livestock Carrier | **TONNAGE:** 8301 | **LAUNCH:** 23 September 1893 |
| **DELIVERY:** 6 January 1894 | **OWNER:** Oceanic Steam Navigation Company (White Star Line) | |

| REF. NO. | DATE | MAIN SUBJECT |
|---|---|---|
| H730-731 | August 1901 | Office display of half models of White Star ships CUFIC/RUNIC (210-211), CEVIC (270) & CELTIC (335). |

| SHIP NO: 280 | | NAME: NORMAN |
|---|---|---|
| **TYPE:** Passenger Ship | **TONNAGE** 7392 | **LAUNCH:** 19 July 1894 |
| **DELIVERY:** 13 October 1894 | **OWNER:** Union Steamship Company | |

| REF. NO. | DATE | MAIN SUBJECT |
|---|---|---|
| H2350 | 19 July 1894 | Launch; port stern ¾ profile entering water from No. 7 slip, North Yard. |
| H2351 | 19 July 1894 | Starboard bow near profile afloat after launch, with paddle tugs manoeuvring. |

| SHIP NO: 284 | | NAME: GUELPH |
|---|---|---|
| **TYPE:** Passenger Ship | **TONNAGE** 4917 | **LAUNCH:** 26 June 1894 |
| **DELIVERY:** 8 September 1894 | **OWNER:** Union Steamship Company | |

| REF. NO. | DATE | MAIN SUBJECT |
|---|---|---|
| H2344 | September 1894 | Starboard bow view of completed ship alongside No. 1 outfitting jetty, Abercorn Basin. |
| H2345 | September 1894 | View aft from forecastle deck towards bridge. |
| H2346 | September 1894 | View aft along starboard promenade deck. |
| H2347 | September 1894 | First class dining saloon. |
| H2348 | September 1894 | First class dining saloon, with piano. |
| H2349 | September 1894 | Second class dining saloon. |

| SHIP NO: 293 | | NAME: GEORGIC |
|---|---|---|
| **TYPE:** Livestock Carrier | **TONNAGE** 10077 | **LAUNCH:** 22 June 1895 |
| **DELIVERY:** 8 August 1895 | **OWNER:** Oceanic Steam Navigation Company (White Star Line) | |

| REF. NO. | DATE | MAIN SUBJECT |
|---|---|---|
| H2336 | c.August 1895 | Starboard bow near profile of cased builder's model. |
| H2336A | c.August 1895 | Starboard profile of cased builder's model. |
| H2337 | c.August 1895 | Starboard stern near profile of cased builder's model. |
| H2338 | 22 June 1895 | Port bow profile on No. 7 slip North Yard prior to launch. |
| H2339 | 22 June 1895 | Port view of rudder and twin propellers prior to launch. |
| H2341 | 22 June 1895 | Launch; port stern view entering water. |
| H2342 | 22 June 1895 | Port bow view afloat immediately after launch. |
| H2343 | c.June 1895 | Starboard bow near profile alongside jetty after launch. |

| SHIP NO: 296 | | NAME: CESTRIAN |
|---|---|---|
| **TYPE:** Passenger Ship | **TONNAGE:** 8761 | **LAUNCH:** 21 September 1895 |
| **DELIVERY:** 5 March 1896 | **OWNER:** F Leyland & Company Limited | |

| REF. NO. | DATE | MAIN SUBJECT |
|---|---|---|
| H2360 | c.March 1896 | Starboard profile of completed ship alongside No. 1 outfitting jetty, Abercorn Basin. |

| SHIP NO: 299 | | NAME: CHINA |
|---|---|---|

| TYPE: | TONNAGE: | LAUNCH: |
|---|---|---|
| Passenger Ship | 7899 | 13 June 1896 |

| DELIVERY: | OWNER: |
|---|---|
| 28 November 1896 | Peninsular & Oriental Steam Navigation Company |

| REF. NO. | DATE | MAIN SUBJECT |
|---|---|---|
| H42 | June 1896 | Port bow view on old No. 8 slip, renumbered 3, North Yard, prior to launch. |
| H44 | 13 June 1896 | Port stern view on slip prior to launch. |
| H46 | 13 June 1896 | Port bow ¾ profile immediately after launch. |
| H356 | 1898 | Alexandra Graving Dock with shores for repair of CHINA, badly damaged March 1898. |
| H357 | 1898 | Alexandra Graving Dock with ship in background, alongside outfitting wharf. |
| H358-363 | 1898 | Sequence showing positioning of ship in flooded graving dock with supporting shores. |
| H364-369 | 1898 | Sequence showing ship in dry dock with shores and cables arranged to support damaged bottom. |
| H370-378 | 1898 | Sequence showing damaged bottom at bow section and means of providing support. |
| H379-383 | 1898 | Sequence showing internal arrangements of supporting timber shores. |
| H384 | 1898 | Port bow view in Alexandra Graving Dock with supporting shores. |
| H394-396 | 1898 | Sequence showing removal of damaged bottom plates. |
| H396A | 1898 | 'Black squad' posed beneath the damaged section of hull. |
| H396C-D | c.March 1898 | Ashore at Perim, an island in the Red Sea, where damage sustained. |
| H397-403 | 1898 | Sequence showing removal of damaged bottom plates. |
| H404 | August 1899 | Underside of hull with damaged plates and frames removed, view forward. |
| H412 | August 1899 | Underside of hull with damaged plates and frames removed, view aft. |
| H413-414 | August 1899 | Stokehold with boilers and damaged plates and frames removed. |
| H415 | 1899 | Propeller and undamaged shell plating, starboard side. |
| H416 | 1899 | Internal arrangement of double bottom where damaged plates removed. |
| H417-418 | 1899 | Replacing damaged bow frames and plates, port and starboard views. |
| H419 | 1899 | Repaired underside hull, starboard bow view from dock floor. |

| SHIP NO: 299 | | NAME: CHINA |
|---|---|---|

| REF. NO. | DATE | MAIN SUBJECT |
|---|---|---|
| H420 | 1899 | Propeller and underside hull, port view forward from dock floor. |
| H421 | 1899 | Starboard bow view of repaired underside hull from side of dry dock. |
| H422 | 1899 | Starboard stern view from side of dry dock, not refitted as above. |
| H423 | 1899 | Port profile, steaming in Belfast Lough after repairs and refitting. |
| H424 | 1899 | Port stern ¾ profile, as above. |
| H425 | 1899 | As above, but more distant. |
| H426 | 1899 | Port stern view in Belfast Lough, with painted-in seagulls and emphasised steam. |

| SHIP NO: 300 | | NAME: CANADA |
|---|---|---|

| TYPE: | TONNAGE: | LAUNCH: |
|---|---|---|
| Passenger Ship | 8800 | 14 May 1896 |

| DELIVERY: | OWNER: |
|---|---|
| 26 September 1896 | Dominion Line |

| REF. NO. | DATE | MAIN SUBJECT |
|---|---|---|
| H40 | 14 May 1896 | Port stern view on old No. 9 slip, renumbered 4, North Yard, prior to launch. |
| H41 | 14 May 1896 | Launch; port stern view entering water. |
| H43 | 14 May 1896 | Bow view afloat immediately after launch. |

| SHIP NO: 302 | | NAME: PENNSYLVANIA | |
|---|---|---|---|
| **TYPE:** Passenger/Cargo Ship | **TONNAGE:** 13726 | **LAUNCH:** 10 September 1896 | |
| **DELIVERY:** 30 January 1897 | | **OWNER:** Hamburg-Amerika Line | |
| REF. NO. | DATE | MAIN SUBJECT | |
| H70 | c.January 1897 | Bow view outfitting and nearing completion, North Yard. | |
| H71 | c.January 1897 | Port stern view outfitting and nearing completion, but with heads and chute on poop. | |
| H72 | c.January 1897 | Starboard profile at outfitting wharf, nearing completion. | |
| H73 | c.January 1897 | Deck view aft from midships superstructure, nearing completion. | |
| H74 | c.January 1897 | Deck view forward from bridge, nearing completion. | |

| SHIP NO: 311 | | NAME: GOORKHA | |
|---|---|---|---|
| **TYPE:** Passenger Ship | **TONNAGE:** 6286 | **LAUNCH:** 23 January 1897 | |
| **DELIVERY:** 28 August 1897 | | **OWNER:** Union Steamship Company | |
| REF. NO. | DATE | MAIN SUBJECT | |
| H62 | 23 January 1897 | Starboard bow profile on renumbered 7 slip, South Yard prior to launch. | |
| H63 | 23 January 1897 | Underside of hull prior to launch, showing cradle and drag chains. | |
| H64 | 23 January 1897 | Naming ceremony, launch party and spectators. | |
| H65 | 23 January 1897 | Bow view immediately after launch with lubricated ways in foreground. | |
| H65B | c.August 1897 | Starboard profile outfitting at No. 1 jetty, Abercorn Basin. | |

| SHIP NO: 304 | | NAME: GASCON | |
|---|---|---|---|
| **TYPE:** Passenger Ship | **TONNAGE:** 6288 | **LAUNCH:** 25 August 1896 | |
| **DELIVERY:** 13 February 1897 | | **OWNER:** Union Steamship Company | |
| REF. NO. | DATE | MAIN SUBJECT | |
| H75 | February 1897 | View aft towards bridge from forecastle deck at sea. | |
| H76 | February 1897 | View aft from port bridge wing, showing funnel, masts and lifeboats, at sea. | |
| H77 | February 1897 | First class dining saloon, with piano | |
| H78 | February 1897 | First class dining saloon. | |
| H79 | February 1897 | First class smoke room. | |
| H80 | February 1897 | Second class dining saloon, with piano. | |
| H81 | February 1897 | Third class dining saloon. | |
| H82 | February 1897 | First class library. | |

| SHIP NO: 312 | | NAME: ROTTERDAM | |
|---|---|---|---|
| **TYPE:** Passenger Ship | **TONNAGE:** 8301 | **LAUNCH:** 18 February 1897 | |
| **DELIVERY:** 29 July 1897 | | **OWNER:** Holland-America Line | |
| REF. NO. | DATE | MAIN SUBJECT | |
| H83 | 18 February 1897 | Port stern view on old No. 6 slip, renumbered 1, North Yard prior to launch. | |
| H84 | 18 February 1897 | Launch; port stern view entering water with propellers turning. | |
| H85 | 18 February 1897 | Port bow ¾ profile, afloat immediately after launch. | |

## SHIP NO: 313     NAME: BRITON

| TYPE: | TONNAGE: | LAUNCH: |
|---|---|---|
| Passenger Ship | 10248 | 5 June 1897 |

| DELIVERY: | OWNER: |
|---|---|
| 26 November 1897 | Union Steamship Company |

| REF. NO. | DATE | MAIN SUBJECT |
|---|---|---|
| H86 | 5 June 1897 | Port stern view on old No. 9 slip, renumbered 4, North Yard prior to launch. |
| H87 | 5 June 1897 | Launch; port stern view entering water. |
| H88 | 5 June 1897 | Launch; port bow ¾ profile afloat immediately after launch. |
| H89 | 5 June 1897 | Launch; port bow ¾ profile moving through water. |
| H201 | November 1897 | Port stern ¾ profile of completed ship alongside wharf. |
| H202 | November 1897 | Bridge and decks viewed from forward deckhouse. |
| H203 | November 1897 | Port boat deck, funnels and engine room skylights, view forward towards bridge. |
| H204 | November 1897 | Port boat deck, funnels and ventilators, view aft from bridge. |
| H205 | November 1897 | Forecastle deck and forward deckhouse viewed from bridge. |
| H206 | November 1897 | Starboard view forward from poop deck. |
| H207 | November 1897 | View aft along starboard promenade deck. |
| H208 | November 1897 | First class dining saloon, with cloths on tables. |
| H208A | November 1897 | First class dining saloon without cloths on tables. |
| H209 | November 1897 | First class dining saloon with ceiling dome and frieze. |
| H210 | November 1897 | Second class dining saloon, with panelled sides and bare steel ceiling. |
| H211 | November 1897 | First class smoke room with ceiling dome. |
| H212 | November 1897 | First class library with ceiling dome. |
| H213 | November 1897 | Dome and frieze above first class staircase. |

## SHIP NO: 314     NAME: DERBYSHIRE

| TYPE: | TONNAGE: | LAUNCH: |
|---|---|---|
| Passenger Ship | 6635 | 21 July 1897 |

| DELIVERY: | OWNER: |
|---|---|
| 8 October 1897 | Bibby Steamship Company |

| REF. NO. | DATE | MAIN SUBJECT |
|---|---|---|
| H2361 | c.October 1897 | Port stern view of almost completed ship alongside outfitting wharf, North Yard. |

## SHIP NO: 315     NAME: NEW ENGLAND

| TYPE: | TONNAGE: | LAUNCH: |
|---|---|---|
| Passenger Ship | 11394 | 7 April 1898 |

| DELIVERY: | OWNER: |
|---|---|
| 30 June 1898 | Dominion Line, Richard Mills & Company, Managers |

| REF. NO. | DATE | MAIN SUBJECT |
|---|---|---|
| H214 | June 1898 | Bridge and decks viewed from forward deckhouse during trials/delivery. |
| H215 | June 1898 | Officer and civilian adjusting standard compass amidships at sea. |
| H216 | June 1898 | View forward from bridge at sea. |
| H217 | June 1898 | View along promenade deck at sea. |
| H218 | June 1898 | View aft from forecastle deck towards bridge, at sea. |
| H219 | June 1898 | Port boat deck, funnel and engine room skylights, view forward at sea. |
| H221-222 | June 1898 | First class dining saloon with dome frieze. |
| H223 | June 1898 | Dome and frieze above first class dining saloon. |
| H224-226 | June 1898 | First class library. |
| H227 | June 1898 | First class smoke room. |
| H227A | June 1898 | Starboard stern ¾ profile of ship at sea, with smoking funnel. |
| H233 | June 1898 | First class library and stairwell balustrade. |

## SHIP NO: 316     NAME: CYMRIC

| TYPE: | TONNAGE: | LAUNCH: |
|---|---|---|
| Passenger Ship | 12551 | 12 October 1897 |

| DELIVERY: | OWNER: |
|---|---|
| 5 February 1898 | Oceanic Navigation Company (White Star Line) |

| REF. NO. | DATE | MAIN SUBJECT |
|---|---|---|
| H90 | 12 October 1897 | Port bow profile on old No. 8 slip, renumbered 3, North Yard prior to launch. |
| H91 | 12 October 1897 | Rudder and port propeller prior to launch. |
| H92 | 12 October 1897 | Launch; port stern view entering water. |
| H93 | 12 October 1897 | Launch; port bow view entering water. |

| SHIP NO: 317 | | NAME: OCEANIC |
|---|---|---|
| **TYPE:** Passenger Ship | **TONNAGE:** 17274 | **LAUNCH:** 14 January 1899 |
| **DELIVERY:** 26 August 1899 | **OWNER:** Oceanic Steam Navigation Company (White Star Line) | |

| REF. NO. | DATE | MAIN SUBJECT |
|---|---|---|
| H1-H17 | 1 October 1896-1 March 1897 | Reconstruction of North Yard No. 8 slip, renumbered 2, for building OCEANIC. |
| H18-H32 | 1 March 1897-1 October 1897 | Construction of OCEANIC from keel laying to bottoming. |
| H34 | 3 November 1897 | Erecting frames, working from stern forward. Bow view to stern. |
| H36 | 3 November 1897 | Erected stern frames. View from water side of slip. |
| H37 | 3 November 1897 | Timber staging around stern frames. |
| H38 | 3 November 1897 | Erected stern frames and posed workers viewed from tank top. |
| H39 | 3 November 1897 | View forward from inside stern frames. |
| H94 | c.1897 | Condensers and other propelling machinery components in Engine Works erecting shop. |
| H101 | 1 December 1897 | Erecting midship frames, working from stern forward. Bow view to stern. |
| H102 | 1 December 1897 | Frames erected to midships. Port stern view from water side of slip. |
| H103 | 1 December 1897 | View from tank top of frames erected to midships. |
| H104 | 1 December 1897 | View forward from inside stern frames. |
| H105 | 3 January 1898 | Erecting frames forward of midships. Bow view to stern. |
| H106 | 3 January 1898 | Erecting frames. Port stern view from water side of slip. |
| H107 | 3 January 1898 | View from tank top to frames erected forward of midships. |
| H108 | 3 January 1898 | View forward along tank top within erected frames. |
| H110 | 1 February 1898 | Ship framed. Port stern view from water side of slip. |
| H111 | 1 February 1898 | Ship framed. Internal view along tank top. |
| H112 | 1 February 1898 | Ship framed. Internal view along tank top. |
| H113 | 1 February 1898 | Ship framed. Internal view along tank top. |
| H115 | 1 February 1898 | Ship framed. View cross upper deck beams from stern forward. |
| H116 | 1 March 1898 | Shell plating hull. View of bow shrouded in timber staging. |
| H117 | 1 March 1898 | Shell plating portside hull above propeller shaft, with timber staging. |

| SHIP NO: 317 | | NAME: OCEANIC |
|---|---|---|

| REF. NO. | DATE | MAIN SUBJECT |
|---|---|---|
| H118 | 1 March 1898 | General view, shell plating portside hull aft of midships. |
| H119 | 1 March 1898 | Hydraulic riveter suspended from gantry. View aft across upper deck beams. |
| H120 | 1 March 1898 | Erection of main engine frames on bedplates in Engine Works. |
| H121 | 1 March 1898 | As above, but from opposite end of engines. |
| H122 | 1 April 1898 | Plating upper deck, view aft. |
| H123 | 1 April 1898 | Plating upper deck, view forward. |
| H124 | 1 April 1898 | General view, shell plating portside hull forward of midships. |
| H125 | 1 April 1898 | General view, shell plating portside hull aft of midships. |
| H126 | 1 April 1898 | Electric driller working on topside shell plating. |
| H127 | 1 April 1898 | Hydraulic riveter working on topside shell plating. |
| H128 | 1 May 1898 | Man operating a portable electric driller on main deck within the hull. |
| H129 | 1 May 1898 | Plating main deck within the hull, view aft. |
| H131 | 1 May 1898 | Shell plating portside hull amidships. |
| H132 | 1 June 1898 | Bow view during plating, flanked by 322 and 323 on adjacent slips. |
| H133 | 1 June 1898 | General view, shell plating portside hull forward of midships. |
| H134 | 1 June 1898 | Shell plating starboard propeller shaft and bossing. |
| H135 | 1 June 1898 | Plating under deck, view forward. |
| H136 | 1 June 1898 | Erection of main engines; cylinder castings alongside. |
| H137 | 1 June 1898 | As above, but from opposite end of engines. |
| H138 | 1 July 1898 | Hydraulic riveter working on upper deck plating, view forward. |
| H139 | 1 July 1898 | Hydraulic riveter working on upper deck plating between beams 77 & 78. |
| H140 | c.1 July 1898 | Completed shell plating of starboard propeller shaft and bossing. |
| H141 | 1 July 1898 | General view, completed shell plating portside hull forward of midships. |
| H142 | 1 July 1898 | Crankshaft and other propelling machinery components in Engine Works prior to assembly. |
| H143 | 1 July 1898 | Condensers and other propelling machinery components in Engine Works prior to assembly. |
| H144 | 1 July 1898 | Drive shafts in Engine Works prior to assembly. |
| H145 | 1 July 1898 | Thrust shaft on lathe in Engine Works. |
| H146 | 1 July 1898 | Boilers in course of construction in Engine Works boiler shop. |

| REF. NO. | DATE | MAIN SUBJECT |
|---|---|---|
| H147 | 1 July 1898 | As above, but including interior view of boiler shell. |
| H148 | 1 August 1898 | Starboard bow view on slip, with timber staging and shell plating complete. |
| H149 | 1 August 1898 | Port stern view from water side of slip, with timber staging and shell plating complete. |
| H150 | 1 August 1898 | Plating upper deck, view aft. |
| H151 | 1 August 1898 | Plating upper deck, view forward. |
| H152 | 1 August 1898 | Erection of main engines; beginning to mount cylinders. |
| H153 | 1 August 1898 | As above, but from opposite end of engines. |
| H154 | September 1898 | General view of plated starboard hull aft of midships, including deck. |
| H155 | September 1898 | Structural arrangements within hull, including timber pattern. |
| H156 | September 1898 | Beginning erection of deckhouse on upper deck, view forward. |
| H157 | September 1898 | Laying deck planking forward. Good view of gantry crane, view aft. |
| H158 | 1 October 1898 | Overhead view from gantry crane aft of midships. Also views of ships 322 & 323. |
| H159 | 1 October 1898 | Deckhouses on upper deck in course of erection, view forward. |
| H160 | 1 October 1898 | Hydraulic riveter working on topside shell plating. |
| H161 | 1 October 1898 | Line boring port propeller shaft bearing from outside hull. |
| H162-164 | 1 October 1898 | Erection of main engines; crankshaft arrangement. |
| H165 | 1 October 1898 | Turning main engine crankshaft journal on Engine Works lathe. |
| H166-167 | 1 October 1898 | Boilers in course of construction. |
| H168 | November 1898 | Forward deck with block, tackle and sheerleg arrangement in foreground, view aft. |
| H169 | November 1898 | Laying steel deck plating over deckhouses on upper deck. |
| H170-171 | November 1898 | Internal structural arrangement of deckhouse and promenade on upper deck. |
| H172-173 | November 1898 | Erection of main engines; cylinders in place. |
| H174 | November 1898 | Boilers in course of construction. |
| H175 | November 1898 | Internal view of boiler shell. |
| H176 | December 1898 | Port bow view of light grey painted hull, surrounded by timber staging. |
| H177-178 | November 1898 | Tailshaft mounted on bogeys outside Engine Works. |
| H179 | December 1898 | Forward deck with capstans in foreground, also timber deck planking, view aft. |

| REF. NO. | DATE | MAIN SUBJECT |
|---|---|---|
| H180 | December 1898 | Afterdeck with deck planking, windlasses and deckhouse, view forward. |
| H181 | December 1898 | Timber shoring and trackway beneath hull at turn of the bilge. |
| H182-183 | December 1898 | Erection of main engines; pistons, connecting rods etc, in position. |
| H184 | December 1898 | Boilers in course of construction. |
| H185 | December 1898 | Portable boring machine set up in furnace of boiler during construction. |
| H186 | January 1899 | Starboard bow ¾ profile on slip prior to launch. Topside hull painted light grey. |
| H187 | January 1899 | Starboard bow profile prior to launch, with shoring and forward part of cradle. |
| H188 | January 1899 | Complete bow view prior to launch. |
| H189 | January 1899 | Port stern profile prior to launch, with counter, rudder, propeller and bossing. |
| H190 | January 1899 | Close-up of portside propeller, with shipwright standing on adjacent staging. |
| H191 | February 1899 | Starboard profile fitting out at Alexandra Wharf, with 100 ton crane. |
| H192 | February 1899 | Port bow ¾ profile fitting out at Alexandra Wharf. |
| H193 | January 1899 | Portable boilers and shipwrights laying deck prior to launch. |
| H194 | January 1899 | Erection of main engines; fitting steam pipes and cylinder heads. |
| H195 | January 1899 | Erection of auxiliary reciprocating machinery. |
| H196-197 | January 1899 | Boilers in course of construction. |
| H198 | February 1899 | Outfitting at Alexandra Wharf, view aft over deckhouses. |
| H199 | February 1899 | Installation of auxiliary machinery in engine room, prior to main engines. |
| H200 | February 1899 | Alongside outfitting wharf with 100 ton crane lifting machinery bed on board. |
| H242 | c.August 1899 | Office display of half models of White Star liner OCEANIC (73), MAJESTIC (209) and OCEANIC (II, 317). |
| H245 | 14 January 1899 | Starboard bow profile immediately prior to launch, with slung cables and anchors. |
| H246 | 14 January 1899 | Port stern view immediately prior to launch. |
| H247 | 14 January 1899 | As above, but closer. |
| H248 | 14 January 1899 | Port stern view and spectators immediately prior to launch. |

| SHIP NO: 317 | | NAME: OCEANIC |
|---|---|---|
| REF. NO. | DATE | MAIN SUBJECT |
| H249 | 14 January 1899 | Detail of rudder and portside propeller immediately prior to launch. |
| H250 | 14 January 1899 | Launch; port stern view entering water. |
| H250A | 14 January 1899 | Launch; port stern entering water with propellers revolving. |
| H251 | 14 January 1899 | Port bow view afloat immediately after launch. |
| H252 | 14 January 1899 | Port bow ¾ profile afloat immediately after launch. |
| H252-254 | 14 January 1899 | Launching trigger, pump and pressure gauge on ways immediately after launch. |
| H255 | 14 January 1899 | View down greased ways after launch with OCEANIC and tugs in background. |
| H256 | February 1899 | Installation of boilers in stokehold with posed workers. |
| H257 | March 1899 | View aft from forecastle deck towards bridge during outfitting at Alexandra Wharf. |
| H258 | March 1899 | 100 ton outfitting crane lifting funnel section on board. |
| H259 | March 1899 | Lifeboats lying on after boatdeck during outfitting. Shipwrights in foreground. |
| H260 | March 1899 | View along promenade deck during outfitting. |
| H261 | March 1899 | Funnel section on outfitting wharf prior to being lifted on board. |
| H262 | March 1899 | Installation of both sets of main engines in engine room. |
| H263 | 1 April 1899 | View aft from forecastle deck towards bridge during outfitting. |
| H264 | 1 April 1899 | View forward from poop deck towards after boat deck during outfitting. |
| H265 | 1 April 1899 | Joinery and panelling work on first class staircase during outfitting. |
| H266 | 1 April 1899 | Initial work on outfitting first class dining saloon. |
| H267 | 1 April 1899 | Port stern view alongside outfitting wharf, with after funnel in position. |
| H268 | 1 April 1899 | Stokehold fans and base of after funnel during outfitting. |
| H269 | 1 April 1899 | Port bow ¾ profile during outfitting, from south side of Alexandra Graving Dock. |
| H270 | 1 April 1899 | Portside upper promenade deck during outfitting. |
| H271 | 1 May 1899 | Starboard stern ¾ profile during outfitting. Both funnels in position. |
| H272-273 | 1 May 1899 | Repainting port hull from light grey to black during outfitting. |

| SHIP NO: 317 | | NAME: OCEANIC |
|---|---|---|
| REF. NO. | DATE | MAIN SUBJECT |
| H274 | 1 May 1899 | Vessel berthed away from side of outfitting wharf by means of pontoons, for painting. |
| H275-280 | 1 June 1899 | Dome and decorated panels of first class dining saloon during outfitting. |
| H281 | 1 June 1899 | View forward from after boat deck towards funnels during outfitting. |
| H282 | 1 June 1899 | Starboard boat deck with lifeboats under davits, workers and funnels during outfitting. |
| H283 | 1 June 1899 | View aft from foremast showing boat decks, funnel and wheelhouse under construction. |
| H284 | 1 June 1899 | View aft along starboard side while outfitting. |
| H285 | 1 June 1899 | View forward along starboard side while outfitting. |
| H286 | 1 July 1899 | Port profile while outfitting at Alexandra Wharf. |
| H287 | 1 July 1899 | View aft from forecastle deck rail towards bridge, during outfitting. |
| H288 | 1 July 1899 | View aft from forecastle deck hatch towards bridge, with windlasses and mast in foreground. |
| H289 | 1 July 1899 | View forward from after funnel towards fore funnel and bridge. |
| H290 | 1 August 1899 | Collier bunkering ship at Alexandra Wharf in final stage of outfitting. |
| H291 | 1 August 1899 | View forward from after end of boat deck towards funnels during outfitting. |
| H292 | 1 August 1899 | Engine room skylights, boat deck and funnels. |
| H293 | 1 August 1899 | View forward from bridge across forecastle deck. |
| H294 | August 1899 | View aft along portside promenade deck. |
| H295 | August 1899 | View forward along starboard promenade deck at library, during trials. |
| H296 | August 1899 | Funnels and portside boat deck from bridge, while at outfitting wharf. |
| H297 | August 1899 | Bridge, telegraphs, officers and wheelhouse from starboard bridge wing. |
| H298 | August 1899 | View forward from bridge across forecastle deck while at outfitting wharf. |
| H299 | August 1899 | Anchor cables and capstans on forecastle deck. |
| H300 | August 1899 | View forward along starboard promenade deck including funnels and boat deck. |
| H301 | August 1899 | Staircase and door to first class library. |
| H302 | August 1899 | Door and entrance to first class library, from inside. |
| H303 | August 1899 | Staircase, landing and door to first class library. |
| H304 | August 1899 | Landing and seating outside first class library. |
| H305-306 | August 1899 | First class library corner seating and panelling. |

| SHIP NO: 317 | | NAME: OCEANIC |
|---|---|---|
| REF. NO. | DATE | MAIN SUBJECT |
| H307 | August 1899 | Side view of first class library, looking aft. |
| H308 | August 1899 | First class library tables and ceiling. |
| H309 | August 1899 | Central table and dome of first class library. |
| H310 | August 1899 | First class dining saloon, including piano. |
| H311 | August 1899 | First class dining saloon, including organ. |
| H312 | August 1899 | First class dining saloon. |
| H313 | August 1899 | First class dining saloon stair corner. |
| H314 | August 1899 | General view of first class dining saloon, including panels below dome. |
| H315 | August 1899 | Dome above first class entrance aft. |
| H316 | August 1899 | Corner of first class entrance, including staircase. |
| H317 | August 1899 | First class entrance viewed from staircase. |
| H318 | August 1899 | Ornately decorated door, wall and ceiling of first class smoke room. |
| H319 | August 1899 | Cherubic figures and doorway of a first class public room. |
| H320 | August 1899 | Corner of second class library. |
| H321 | August 1899 | General view of second class dining saloon. |
| H322 | August 1899 | Corner of second class smoke room. |
| H323-324 | August 1899 | First class state room. |
| H325 | August 1899 | First class aft state room. |
| H326 | August 1899 | General view of first class smoke room. |
| H327 | August 1899 | Corner of first class smoke room. |
| H328-329 | August 1899 | Dome and decorated panels of first class smoke room. |
| H330 | August 1899 | Wall panel in first class smoke room depicting landing of Columbus in America. |
| H331 | August 1899 | Voyage of Columbus triptych in first class smoke room. |
| H332 | August 1899 | Wall panel in first class smoke room depicting reception of Columbus in Spain. |
| H333-334 | August 1899 | Steering gear and rudder head. |
| H335 | August 1899 | Engine room, looking down on cylinder heads. |
| H336 | August 1899 | Engine room from cylinder heads catwalk. |
| H337 | August 1899 | Engine room well and skylight from catwalk. |
| H338 | August 1899 | Dome and decorated panels of first class smoke room. |
| H339 | August 1899 | Decorated panels below dome of first class smoke room. |
| H340 | August 1899 | View forward from poop deck. |
| H341 | August 1899 | First class staircase and entrance below. |

| SHIP NO: 317 | | NAME: OCEANIC |
|---|---|---|
| REF. NO. | DATE | MAIN SUBJECT |
| H342-342A | August 1899 | Portside profile of completed ship at outfitting wharf. |
| H343-343A | August 1899 | Portside profile of completed ship at outfitting wharf, with list to port. |
| H344 | August 1899 | Details of first class library ceiling. |
| H345-347 | November 1899 | Cased builder's model, complete with gun on forecastle deck. |
| H569 | c.January 1899 | Port bow view on slip prior to launch with round timber rack in foreground. |

| SHIP NO: 320 | | NAME: STATENDAM |
|---|---|---|
| TYPE: Passenger Ship | TONNAGE: 10319 | LAUNCH: 7 May 1898 |
| DELIVERY: 18 August 1898 | | OWNER: Holland-America Line |
| REF. NO. | DATE | MAIN SUBJECT |
| H220 | August 1898 | Starboard bow view of completed ship being manoeuvred by tugs at Alexandra outfitting wharf. |
| H228 | August 1898 | Port stern view of ship being manoeuvred into Alexandra Graving Dock. |
| H229 | August 1898 | Bow view of ship entering Alexandra Graving Dock. |

| SHIP NO: 322 | | NAME: AFRIC |
|---|---|---|
| TYPE: Passenger/Cargo Ship | TONNAGE: 11948 | LAUNCH: 16 November 1898 |
| DELIVERY: 2 February 1899 | | OWNER: Oceanic Steam Navigation Company (White Star Line) |
| REF. NO. | DATE | MAIN SUBJECT |
| H132 | 1 June 1898 | Bow view in frame on No. 3 slip, North Yard, adjacent (left) to OCEANIC on No. 2 slip. |
| H158 | 1 October 1898 | Overhead view of steel deck laying on after part of hull, from gantry crane. |

| SHIP NO: 323 | | NAME: MEDIC | |
|---|---|---|---|
| **TYPE:** | | **TONNAGE:** | **LAUNCH:** |
| Passenger/Cargo Ship | | 11985 | 15 December 1898 |
| **DELIVERY:** | | **OWNER:** | |
| 6 July 1899 | | Oceanic Steam Navigation Company (White Star Line) | |

| REF. NO. | DATE | MAIN SUBJECT |
|---|---|---|
| H131 | 1 May 1898 | Tank top with OCEANIC (317) in background. |
| H132 | 1 June 1898 | Bow view in frame on No. 1 slip, North Yard, adjacent (right) to OCEANIC on No. 2 slip. |
| H158 | 1 October 1898 | Overhead view of steel deck laying on after part of hull, from gantry crane. |
| H385 | c.July 1899 | Third class general room (saloon). |
| H386 | c.July 1899 | Third class smoke room. |
| H387-387A | c.July 1899 | Third class mess room (dining saloon). |
| H388 | c.July 1899 | Third class 4-berth cabin. |
| H389 | c.July 1899 | Third class 20-berth cabin. |
| H390-391 | c.July 1899 | Passageway, top of staircase and cabin doors. |
| H392 | July 1899 | View forward from after end of port boat deck with engine room skylights in foreground. |
| H393 | July 1899 | View forward from after deck towards port boat deck. |
| H393A | July 1899 | View forward from poop deck across after deck hatches towards boat deck. |

| SHIP NO: 324 | | NAME: WINIFREDIAN | |
|---|---|---|---|
| **TYPE:** | | **TONNAGE:** | **LAUNCH:** |
| Passenger Ship | | 10404 | 11 March 1899 |
| **DELIVERY:** | | **OWNER:** | |
| 8 July 1899 | | F Leyland & Company Limited | |

| REF. NO. | DATE | MAIN SUBJECT |
|---|---|---|
| H351 | March 1899 | Stern view on No. 5 slip, South Yard, prior to launch. |
| H352 | 11 March 1899 | Launch; starboard stern view entering water. |
| H352A | 11 March 1899 | Launch; view of starboard bow entering water with empty slip in background. |
| H353 | 11 March 1899 | Port profile afloat in Abercorn Basin, after launch. |
| H354 | 11 March 1899 | Starboard bow view afloat immediately after launch. |
| H405 | July 1899 | Starboard stern near profile of completed ship at outfitting jetty, Abercorn Basin. |
| H406 | July 1899 | View aft from forward hatch towards bridge. |
| H407 | July 1899 | View aft along port promenade deck. |
| H408 | July 1899 | View aft along port boat deck. |
| H409 | July 1899 | Dining saloon for 135 saloon passengers. |
| H410 | July 1899 | Library for 135 saloon passengers. |
| H411 | July 1899 | Smoke room for 135 saloon passengers. |
| H2354 | c.July 1899 | Builder's half model, starboard side. |
| H2354 | c.July 1899 | Builder's half model in model shop with tools and other completed half models. |

| SHIP NO: 325 | | NAME: PERSIC | |
|---|---|---|---|
| **TYPE:** | | **TONNAGE:** | **LAUNCH:** |
| Passenger/Cargo Ship | | 11975 | 7 September 1899 |
| **DELIVERY:** | | **OWNER:** | |
| 16 November 1899 | | Oceanic Steam Navigation Company (White Star Line) | |

| REF. NO. | DATE | MAIN SUBJECT |
|---|---|---|
| H348-349 | 7 September 1899 | Starboard stern view on No. 7 slip, South Yard, prior to launch. |
| H350 | 7 September 1899 | Starboard profile, afloat in Abercorn Basin immediately after launch. |

| SHIP NO: 326 | | NAME: SAXON |
|---|---|---|
| **TYPE:** | **TONNAGE:** | **LAUNCH:** |
| Passenger Ship | 12385 | 21 December 1899 |
| **DELIVERY:** | | **OWNER:** |
| 9 June 1900 | | Union Steamship Company |

| REF. NO. | DATE | MAIN SUBJECT |
|---|---|---|
| H455 | 21 December 1899 | Starboard bow profile on No. 6 slip, South Yard, prior to launch. |
| H456 | 21 December 1899 | Port bow view with launch party on platform prior to launch. |
| H457 | 21 December 1899 | Starboard bow ¾ profile afloat in Abercorn Basin immediately after launch. |
| H651 | June 1900 | First class library. |
| H652-654 | June 1900 | Dome, decorated panels and frieze of first class dining saloon. |
| H655 | June 1900 | First class staircase and landing. |
| H656 | June 1900 | First class hallway, staircase and doorway to saloon. |
| H657 | June 1900 | Second class dining saloon. |
| H658 | June 1900 | Second class smoke room. |
| H659 | June 1900 | First class smoke room. |
| H660-661 | June 1900 | First class cabins with single and double beds. |
| H662-663 | June 1900 | Starboard bow ¾ profile at sea. |
| H664 | June 1900 | Starboard profile at sea. |
| H665 | June 1900 | Starboard bow ¾ profile at sea. |
| H666 | June 1900 | Third class cabin. |
| H667 | June 1900 | Second class cabin. |

| SHIP NO: 328 | | NAME: MINNEAPOLIS |
|---|---|---|
| **TYPE:** | **TONNAGE:** | **LAUNCH:** |
| Passenger/Cargo Ship | 13401 | 18 November 1899 |
| **DELIVERY:** | | **OWNER:** |
| 29 March 1900 | | Atlantic Transport Company |

| REF. NO. | DATE | MAIN SUBJECT |
|---|---|---|
| H427 | March 1900 | Port view in Alexandra Graving Dock while outfitting. |
| H428 | March 1900 | View aft from forward hatch towards bridge, while in graving dock. |
| H429-430 | March 1900 | First class dining saloon. |
| H431 | March 1900 | First class library. |
| H432 | March 1900 | First class smoke room. |
| H433 | March 1900 | First class 4-berth cabin. |
| H434 | March 1900 | First class stateroom with single brass bed. |
| H435 | March 1900 | Adjoining room to above. |
| H436 | March 1900 | Starboard bow ¾ profile at sea. |
| H437-438 | March 1900 | As above, but closer. |
| H439 | March 1900 | Starboard stern ¾ profile at sea. |

| SHIP NO: 329 | | NAME: MINNEHAHA |
|---|---|---|
| **TYPE:** | **TONNAGE:** | **LAUNCH:** |
| Passenger Ship | 13714 | 31 March 1900 |
| **DELIVERY:** | | **OWNER:** |
| 7 July 1900 | | Atlantic Transport Company |

| REF. NO. | DATE | MAIN SUBJECT |
|---|---|---|
| H440-443 | July 1900 | Various views of twin sets of quadruple expansion engines in engine room. |
| H444 | July 1900 | View aft from starboard bridge wing towards boat deck and funnel, at sea. |
| H445 | July 1900 | View forward from port boat deck towards bridge wing, at sea. |
| H446 | July 1900 | View aft from boat deck towards stern, at sea. |
| H447 | July 1900 | Starboard stern ¾ profile, at sea. |
| H448 | July 1900 | As above, but closer to full profile. |
| H449 | July 1900 | Master and officers on bridge, at sea in Belfast Lough. |

| SHIP NO: 330 | NAME: COMMONWEALTH | |
|---|---|---|
| TYPE: | TONNAGE: | LAUNCH: |
| Passenger Ship | 12096 | 31 May 1900 |
| DELIVERY: | | OWNER: |
| 22 September 1900 | | Dominion Line |

| REF. NO. | DATE | MAIN SUBJECT |
|---|---|---|
| H99 | c.1900 | Propelling machinery components in Engine Works turning shop. |

| SHIP NO: 332 | NAME: RUNIC | |
|---|---|---|
| TYPE: | TONNAGE: | LAUNCH: |
| Passenger Ship | 12482 | 25 October 1900 |
| DELIVERY: | | OWNER: |
| 22 December 1900 | | Oceanic Steam Navigation Company (White Star Line) |

| REF. NO. | DATE | MAIN SUBJECT |
|---|---|---|
| H675 | 25 October 1900 | Starboard view towards bow, on No. 7 slip South Yard, prior to launch. |
| H676 | 25 October 1900 | Starboard stern view on slip prior to launch. |
| H677 | 25 October 1900 | Launch; starboard stern view entering water. |
| H678 | 25 October 1900 | Launch; starboard stern view during launch with propeller blades turning. |
| H679 | 25 October 1900 | Starboard stern view afloat in Abercorn Basin immediately after launch. |
| H679A | 25 October 1900 | Starboard stern view afloat in Abercorn Basin after launch. |
| H680 | 25 October 1900 | Starboard bow ¾ profile alongside outfitting jetty after launch. |

| SHIP NO: 333 | NAME: SUEVIC | |
|---|---|---|
| TYPE: | TONNAGE: | LAUNCH: |
| Passenger Ship | 12531 | 8 December 1900 |
| DELIVERY: | | OWNER: |
| 9 March 1901 | | Oceanic Steam Navigation Company (White Star Line) |

| REF. NO. | DATE | MAIN SUBJECT |
|---|---|---|
| H681-682 | March 1901 | General room, including piano and mast (all passengers third class). |
| H683 | March 1901 | Writing room. |
| H684-685 | March 1901 | Smoke room, with mast passing through floor to ceiling. |
| H686 | March 1901 | Dining saloon. |
| H1168 | 1907 | Shell plating replacement 212 ft long bow section on No. 6 slip, South Yard (port bow view). |
| H1169-1169A | 1907 | Views of after end of replacement bow section on slip. |
| H1170 | 5 October 1907 | Port near profile of replacement bow section on slip prior to launch. |
| H1171 | 5 October 1907 | View of after end of replacement bow section prior to launch. |
| H1172 | 5 October 1907 | Launch; entering water bow first (port bow view). |
| H1173 | 5 October 1907 | Near port profile of replacement bow section afloat immediately after launch. |
| H1174 | October 1907 | After end of completed bow section, preparing for tow to Southampton. |
| H1175 | October 1907 | Port bow view of completed bow section under tow for Southampton. |

| SHIP NO: 334 | | NAME: GERMAN |
|---|---|---|

| TYPE: | TONNAGE: | LAUNCH: |
|---|---|---|
| Passenger Ship | 6763 | 4 August 1898 |

| DELIVERY: | OWNER: |
|---|---|
| 10 November 1898 | Union Steamship Company |

| REF. NO. | DATE | MAIN SUBJECT |
|---|---|---|
| H230-230A | March 1898 | Bow and stern views of vessel completely framed on No. 9 slip South Yard. |
| H231 | November 1898 | Starboard bow ¾ profile, nearing completion at No. 1 outfitting jetty, Abercorn Basin. |
| H232 | November 1898 | First class dining saloon. |
| H234 | November 1898 | First class smoke room. |
| H235 | November 1898 | First class 2 berth cabin. |
| H236 | November 1898 | Second class dining saloon. |
| H237 | November 1898 | Second class smoke room. |
| H238 | November 1898 | Second class 4 berth cabin. |
| H239 | November 1898 | Third class 6 berth cabin. |
| H240 | November 1898 | Third class dining saloon. |
| H240A | November 1898 | Starboard profile, nearing completion at outfitting jetty, Abercorn Basin. |
| H241 | November 1898 | Engine room. |

| SHIP NO: 335 | | NAME: CELTIC |
|---|---|---|

| TYPE: | TONNAGE: | LAUNCH: |
|---|---|---|
| Passenger Ship | 20904 | 4 April 1901 |

| DELIVERY: | OWNER: |
|---|---|
| 11 July 1901 | Oceanic Steam Navigation Company (White Star Line) |

| REF. NO. | DATE | MAIN SUBJECT |
|---|---|---|
| H687 | c.September 1900 | Starboard bow view of plated hull on No. 2 slip, North Yard. |
| H692 | 4 April 1901 | Starboard bow profile on slip prior to launch. |
| H693 | 4 April 1901 | Starboard bow ¾ profile on slip prior to launch. |
| H694 | 4 April 1901 | Port stern view on slip prior to launch. |
| H695 | 4 April 1901 | Launch; stern ¾ profile, entering water. |
| H696 | 4 April 1901 | Port bow ¾ view, afloat after launch. |
| H698 | 4 April 1901 | Distant bow view from vacated slip after launch. |
| H699 | April 1901 | Starboard profile fitting out at Alexandra Wharf, with 100 ton crane. |
| H730-731 | August 1901 | Office display of half models of White Star ships CUFIC/RUNIC (210 & 211), CEVIC (270) and CELTIC (335). |
| H732 | July 1901 | Second class library. |
| H733 | July 1901 | Second class dining saloon. |
| H734 | July 1901 | Third class dining saloon/general room. |
| H735 | July 1901 | First class dining saloon. |
| H736 | July 1901 | First class library. |
| H737 | July 1901 | First class smoke room. |
| H738 | July 1901 | First class cabin with single bed. |
| H739 | July 1901 | First class entrance and staircase from below. |
| H742 | 11 July 1901 | Starboard stern ¾ profile at sea with White Star houseflag. |
| H767-769 | c.March 1899 | Laying keel plates, centre plates and bottom plates aft. |

| SHIP NO: 336 | | NAME: RYNDAM |
|---|---|---|
| TYPE: | TONNAGE: | LAUNCH: |
| Passenger Ship | 12302 | 18 May 1901 |
| DELIVERY: | | OWNER: |
| 3 October 1901 | | Holland-America Line |

| REF. NO. | DATE | MAIN SUBJECT |
|---|---|---|
| H671-674 | c.October 1901 | Cased builder's model, various views. |
| H743 | October 1901 | First class dining saloon. |
| H744-745 | October 1901 | First class smoke room, with fireplace. |
| H746 | October 1901 | First class public room with harmonium. |
| H747-747A | October 1901 | First class public room with dome, piano and fireplace. |
| H749-750 | October 1901 | First class staircase and landing, with dome. |

| SHIP NO: 337 | | NAME: CEDRIC |
|---|---|---|
| TYPE: | TONNAGE: | LAUNCH: |
| Passenger Ship | 21073 | 21 August 1902 |
| DELIVERY: | | OWNER: |
| 31 January 1903 | | Oceanic Steam Navigation Company (White Star Line) |

| REF. NO. | DATE | MAIN SUBJECT |
|---|---|---|
| H759 | 21 August 1902 | Port bow profile on No. 3 slip, North Yard, prior to launch. |
| H760 | 21 August 1902 | Port bow ¾ profile prior to launch — good view of ship and yard. |
| H761 | 21 August 1902 | Port bow view prior to launch with workers on board — unusual view from below. |
| H762 | 21 August 1902 | Port stern view immediately prior to launch. |
| H763-763A | 21 August 1902 | Launch; port stern view entering water. |
| H764 | 21 August 1902 | Port bow ¾ profile, afloat immediately after launch. |
| H765 | c.April 1902 | Port bow view on slip with shell plating nearing completion. |
| H766 | c.April 1902 | Port bow profile on slip with shell plating nearing completion. |
| H770 | c.September 1902 | Starboard bow view outfitting at Alexandra Wharf with BRITANNIC (83) alongside. |
| H771-771A | c.September 1902 | Starboard profile outfitting at Alexandra Wharf with BRITANNIC (83) alongside. |
| H772 | January 1903 | First class entrance and staircase. |
| H773 | January 1903 | First class library. |
| H774 | January 1903 | First class smoke room |
| H775 | January 1903 | Window, wall covering and frieze, first class smoke room. |
| H776-777 | January 1903 | First class dining saloon. |
| H778 | January 1903 | Second class library. |
| H779 | January 1903 | Third class dining saloon and general room. |
| H780 | January 1903 | View aft, port side boat deck, ship at sea. |

| SHIP NO: 339 | NAME: MINNETONKA | |
|---|---|---|
| TYPE: | TONNAGE: | LAUNCH: |
| Passenger Ship | 13397 | 12 December 1901 |
| DELIVERY: | OWNER: | |
| 17 May 1902 | Atlantic Transport Company | |

| REF. NO. | DATE | MAIN SUBJECT |
|---|---|---|
| H96 | c.1901 | Propelling machinery components in Engine Works erecting shop. |

| SHIP NO: 340 | NAME: ARABIC (MINNEWASKA) | |
|---|---|---|
| TYPE: | TONNAGE: | LAUNCH: |
| Passenger Ship | 15801 | 18 December 1902 |
| DELIVERY: | OWNER: | |
| 21 June 1903 | Oceanic Steam Navigation Company (White Star Line) | |

| REF. NO. | DATE | MAIN SUBJECT |
|---|---|---|
| H821 | June 1903 | First class entrance and staircase. |
| H822 | June 1903 | First class library. |
| H823 | June 1903 | First class smoke room. |
| H824 | June 1903 | First class dining saloon. |
| H825 | June 1903 | Second class dining saloon. |
| H826 | June 1903 | Second class library. |
| H827 | June 1903 | View aft from bridge to passenger superstructure, promenade decks and funnel while at sea. |
| H828 | June 1903 | Second class smoke room. |

| SHIP NO: 341 | NAME: ATHENIC | |
|---|---|---|
| TYPE: | TONNAGE: | LAUNCH: |
| Passenger Ship | 12234 | 17 August 1901 |
| DELIVERY: | OWNER: | |
| 23 January 1902 | Oceanic Steam Navigation Company (White Star Line) | |

| REF. NO. | DATE | MAIN SUBJECT |
|---|---|---|
| H751 | January 1902 | First class staircase and passageway. |
| H752-752A | January 1902 | First class dining saloon. |
| H753 | January 1902 | First class library. |
| H754 | January 1902 | First class smoke room. |
| H755 | January 1902 | Second class dining saloon. |
| H756 | January 1902 | Second class library. |
| H757 | January 1902 | Third class dining saloon. |
| H758 | January 1902 | Pantry, with stacked plates and bowls, hanging jugs, teapots and coffee pots. |

| SHIP NO: 342 | | NAME: WALMER CASTLE (CELT) |
|---|---|---|
| TYPE: | TONNAGE: | LAUNCH: |
| Passenger Ship | 12545 | 6 July 1901 |
| DELIVERY: | OWNER: | |
| 20 February 1902 | Union-Castle Mail Steamship Company | |

| REF. NO. | DATE | MAIN SUBJECT |
|---|---|---|
| H708 | July 1901 | Starboard stern ¾ view on No. 6 slip, South Yard, prior to launch. |
| H711 | 6 July 1901 | Port near-profile view of light grey hull afloat in Abercorn Basin immediately after launch. |
| H712 | 6 July 1901 | Launch party on platform with ribboned bottle immediately before naming ceremony and launch. |
| H713 | 6 July 1901 | Launch party, naming ceremony and bottle breaking on port bow. |
| H714 | February 1902 | Starboard bow ¾ profile at sea. |
| H714A | February 1902 | Starboard profile at sea. |
| H715 | February 1902 | First class entrance and staircase. |
| H716 | February 1902 | First class writing room and library. |
| H717-717A | February 1902 | First class smoke room. |
| H718-719 | February 1902 | First class dining saloon, with cloth covered tables. |
| H720-721 | February 1902 | First class dining saloon, with detail of dome and decorated panels. |
| H722 | February 1902 | Second class smoke room. |
| H723 | February 1902 | Second class dining saloon. |

| SHIP NO: 345 | | NAME: COLUMBUS (later REPUBLIC) |
|---|---|---|
| TYPE: | TONNAGE: | LAUNCH: |
| Passenger Ship | 15378 | 26 February 1903 |
| DELIVERY: | OWNER: | |
| 12 September 1903 | Dominion Line (later Oceanic Steam Navigation Company, White Star Line) | |

| REF. NO. | DATE | MAIN SUBJECT |
|---|---|---|
| H781-782 | September 1903 | Starboard stern ¾ profile steaming out of Belfast Lough. |
| H783 | September 1903 | First class entrance and staircase. |
| H784 | September 1903 | First class dining saloon. |
| H785-786 | September 1903 | First class library. |
| H787 | September 1903 | First class lounge. |
| H788 | September 1903 | Dome, decorated panels and frieze in first class dining saloon. |
| H789 | September 1903 | First class smoke room. |
| H790 | September 1903 | Second class dining saloon. |
| H2306-2306A | c.October 1903 | Starboard profile of cased builder's model in White Star funnel colours. |

| SHIP NO: 347 | | NAME: GALEKA |
|---|---|---|
| TYPE: | TONNAGE: | LAUNCH: |
| Passenger Ship | 6767 | 21 October 1899 |
| DELIVERY: | OWNER: | |
| 23 December 1899 | Union Steamship Company | |

| REF. NO. | DATE | MAIN SUBJECT |
|---|---|---|
| H451 | 21 October 1899 | Starboard bow profile on No. 9 slip, South Yard prior to launch. |
| H452 | 21 October 1899 | Starboard stern view on slip prior to launch. |
| H453 | 21 October 1899 | Launch; starboard stern view entering water. |

| SHIP NO: 350 | | NAME: MARMORA |
|---|---|---|

| TYPE: | TONNAGE: | LAUNCH: |
|---|---|---|
| Passenger Ship | 10522 | 9 April 1903 |

| DELIVERY: | OWNER: |
|---|---|
| 10 November 1903 | Peninsular and Oriental Steam Navigation Company |

| REF. NO. | DATE | MAIN SUBJECT |
|---|---|---|
| H800 | November 1903 | First class entrance and staircase. |
| H801-802 | November 1903 | Harmonium, panelling, columns and decorative figures and panels in first class dining saloon. |
| H803 | November 1903 | First class dining saloon, with long tables, chairs and decorative ceiling. |
| H804-805 | November 1903 | Upper level first class dining saloon with small tables and overhead glass panels/dome. |
| H806 | November 1903 | First class smoke room. |
| H807 | November 1903 | Captain's lower bridge, with telegraphs, officer and lady. |
| H808 | November 1903 | View aft, starboard side from bridge towards boat deck and funnels, while at sea. |
| H809 | November 1903 | Second class smoke room, balcony, balustrade, chairs and small tables. |
| H810 | November 1903 | Second class smoke room. |

| SHIP NO: 352 | | NAME: BALTIC |
|---|---|---|

| TYPE: | TONNAGE: | LAUNCH: |
|---|---|---|
| Passenger Ship | 23875 | 21 November 1903 |

| DELIVERY: | OWNER: |
|---|---|
| 23 June 1904 | Oceanic Steam Navigation Company (White Star Line) |

| REF. NO. | DATE | MAIN SUBJECT |
|---|---|---|
| H791-791A | November 1903 | Starboard bow ¾ profile on No. 2 slip, North Yard, prior to launch. |
| H792 | November 1903 | Bow view on slip prior to launch. |
| H793 | November 1903 | Port bow ¾ profile on slip prior to launch. |
| H794 | November 1903 | Port bow view on slip prior to launch, with KENILWORTH CASTLE (356) plated on No. 1 slip. |
| H795 | 21 November 1903 | Launch; port stern view, entering choppy water. |
| H796 | 21 November 1903 | Port bow view alongside jetty immediately after launch. |
| H861-861A | June 1904 | First class staircase (upper) and landing. |
| H862-862A | June 1904 | First class staircase, entrance and landing. |
| H863-864 | June 1904 | First class library and writing room. |
| H865-866 | June 1904 | Details of first class library panelling, windows, ceiling and lighting. |
| H867 | June 1904 | First class smoke room from corner. |
| H868 | June 1904 | First class smoke room from door. |
| H869-870 | June 1904 | First class dining saloon. |
| H871 | June 1904 | Second class library and writing room. |
| H872 | June 1904 | Second class smoke room. |
| H873 | June 1904 | Second class cabin. |
| H874 | June 1904 | First class state room and adjoining rooms. |
| H875 | June 1904 | Third class dining saloon. |
| H876 | June 1904 | Second class dining saloon. |
| H877 | June 1904 | View forward from after end of port boat deck towards funnels. |
| H878 | June 1904 | View forward from between funnels along port upper promenade deck towards bridge. |
| H879 | June 1904 | View along lower promenade deck. |
| H880-880A | June 1904 | Port profile of completed ship alongside outfitting wharf. |
| H881 | June 1904 | View aft from island bridge to passenger superstructure, promenade decks and funnels. |
| H882 | June 1904 | Starboard bow ¾ profile steaming in Belfast Lough. |

| SHIP NO: 353 | NAME: PRESIDENT LINCOLN (SERVIAN) |
|---|---|

| TYPE: | TONNAGE: | LAUNCH: |
|---|---|---|
| Passenger Ship | 18073 | 8 October 1903 |

| DELIVERY: | OWNER: |
|---|---|
| 14 May 1907 | Hamburg-Amerika Line (vessel ordered by F Leyland & Company (1900) Limited) |

| REF. NO. | DATE | MAIN SUBJECT |
|---|---|---|
| H1121 | May 1907 | Port near profile of completed vessel at North Yard jetty. |

| SHIP NO: 356 | NAME: KENILWORTH CASTLE |
|---|---|

| TYPE: | TONNAGE: | LAUNCH: |
|---|---|---|
| Passenger Ship | 12975 | 5 December 1903 |

| DELIVERY: | OWNER: |
|---|---|
| 14 May 1904 | Union-Castle Mail Steamship Company |

| REF. NO. | DATE | MAIN SUBJECT |
|---|---|---|
| H794 | November 1903 | Starboard bow view, shell plated, on No. 1 slip, North Yard, BALTIC (352) alongside. |
| H816 | 5 December 1903 | Port bow view on slip prior to launch, with launch party on platform. |
| H817 | 5 December 1903 | Starboard bow view on slip prior to launch. |
| H818 | 5 December 1903 | Port bow ¾ profile, afloat immediately after launch. |
| H819 | 5 December 1903 | As above, but more distant view. |
| H819A | 5 December 1903 | Port bow view, afloat after launch and including spectators on jetty. |
| H840 | May 1904 | Port bow ¾ profile of completed ship at sea. |
| H841 | May 1904 | Staircase and entrance to first class dining saloon, with saloon beyond. |
| H842-843 | May 1904 | First class dining saloon. |
| H844 | May 1904 | Second class dining saloon. |
| H845-845A | May 1904 | First class library (same view). |
| H846 | May 1904 | Second class smoke room. |
| H847-847A | May 1904 | First class smoke room (same view). |
| H848 | May 1904 | First class landing and staircase. |
| H2300 | May 1904 | Starboard profile of cased builder's model. |

| SHIP NO: 357 | NAME: AMERIKA | |
|---|---|---|
| TYPE: | TONNAGE: | LAUNCH: |
| Passenger Ship | 22724 | 20 April 1905 |

| DELIVERY: | OWNER: |
|---|---|
| 21 September 1905 | Hamburg-Amerika Line |

| REF. NO. | DATE | MAIN SUBJECT |
|---|---|---|
| H838 | c.November 1904 | Port bow view, shell plating completed, on No. 2 slip, North Yard. |
| H839 | c. November 1904 | View aft from forecastle deck showing other decks under construction. |
| H890 | April 1905 | Bow view on slip preparing for launch. |
| H891-891A | April 1905 | Port bow view on slip prior to launch. |
| H892 | April 1905 | Port bow near profile on slip prior to launch. |
| H896 | 20 April 1905 | Port bow ¾ profile afloat after launch. Spectators and jetty in foreground. |
| H947-948 | September 1905 | First class entrance and staircase. |
| H950-951 | September 1905 | Corner and side of first class dining saloon adjacent to hallway and staircase. |
| H952-952A | September 1905 | First class ladies drawing room. |
| H953 | September 1905 | First class smoke room. |
| H954 | September 1905 | Staircase leading to first class smoke room. |
| H956-957 | September 1905 | First class promenade deck, port and starboard sides. |
| H958-960 | September 1905 | Second class library and writing room. |
| H961-961A | September 1905 | Second class smoke room. |
| H962 | September 1905 | First class lift and staircase. |
| H963 | September 1905 | First class nursery. |
| H2284 | September 1905 | Starboard profile of cased builder's model. |

| SHIP NO: 358 | NAME: ADRIATIC | |
|---|---|---|
| TYPE: | TONNAGE: | LAUNCH: |
| Passenger Ship | 24540 | 20 September 1906 |

| DELIVERY: | OWNER: |
|---|---|
| 25 April 1907 | Oceanic Steam Navigation Company (White Star Line) |

| REF. NO. | DATE | MAIN SUBJECT |
|---|---|---|
| H970 | 30 January 1906 | Port bow profile during shell plating on No. 3 slip, North Yard. |
| H971-972 | 30 January 1906 | Laying main and upper deck plates. |
| H973 | c.February 1906 | Port bow profile during shell plating. |
| H974 | c.February 1906 | Starboard bow profile during shell plating. |
| H975 | c.February 1906 | Laying main deck plates, with posed workers. |
| H976 | c.March 1906 | Port bow view during shell plating. |
| H977 | c.March 1906 | Laying main deck plates. |
| H978 | c.March 1906 | Internal view showing hatchways with posed workers. |
| H979 | c.March 1906 | Laying upper deck plates, with posed workers. |
| H980 | c.June 1906 | Elevated view of North Yard from B crane with starboard bow ¾ profile of 358 under construction. |
| H981 | June 1906 | Port bow view on slip with shell plating completed. Length of angle iron in foreground. |
| H982-983 | June 1906 | Construction of deck houses and bolting upper deck plates prior to riveting. |
| H985 | c.July 1906 | View aft from installed fittings on forecastle deck. |
| H986 | c.July 1906 | Internal view along main deck, with subdivision of space beginning. |
| H987 | September 1906 | Starboard stern ¾ profile on slip prior to launch. View across Victoria Channel. |
| H988 | September 1906 | Port bow view on slip prior to launch. |
| H989 | September 1906 | Port bow ¾ profile on slip prior to launch. Plates and steam crane in foreground. |
| H989A | September 1906 | As above, but without crane and slightly different view. |
| H990 | September 1906 | Port bow profile on slip prior to launch. |
| H991-991A | 20 September 1906 | Launch; port stern view entering water. |
| H992, 992A, 993 | 20 September 1906 | Port bow ¾ profile afloat immediately after launch. |
| H994-995 | April 1907 | Port profile of completed ship alongside outfitting wharf. |
| H996 | April 1907 | Captain's bridge, wheel and telegraphs, viewed from starboard bridge wing. |
| H997 | April 1907 | First class entrance and down staircase. |

| SHIP NO: 358 | | NAME: ADRIATIC |
|---|---|---|
| REF. NO. | DATE | MAIN SUBJECT |
| H998 | April 1907 | First class enquiries office, leading to purser's office. |
| H999 | April 1907 | First class lounge/writing room and library. |
| H1001-1002 | April 1907 | First class ladies reading room. |
| H1003 | April 1907 | First class dining saloon. |
| H1004 | April 1907 | First class dining saloon, details of panelling and plasterwork. |
| H1005-1006 | April 1907 | First class smoke room and writing room. |
| H1007 | April 1907 | First class Turkish bath cooling room. |
| H1008 | April 1907 | First class plunge bath. |
| H1009 | April 1907 | Second class dining saloon. |
| H1122 | April 1907 | Second class library, with mast passing through floor to ceiling. |
| H1123 | April 1907 | Second class smoke room, with mast passing through floor to ceiling. |
| H1124 | April 1907 | Staircase leading down to second class lounge. |
| H1125 | April 1907 | Third class dining saloon. |
| H1126 | April 1907 | First class ladies room, including fireplace. |
| H1127 | April 1907 | First class library. |
| H2283-2283A | April 1907 | Starboard profile of cased builder's model. |

| SHIP NO: 360 | | NAME: HMS ENCHANTRESS | |
|---|---|---|---|
| TYPE: Steam Yacht | | TONNAGE: 2514 | LAUNCH: 7 November 1903 |
| DELIVERY: 11 June 1904 | | | OWNER: Admiralty |
| REF. NO. | DATE | MAIN SUBJECT | |
| H811 | 7 November 1903 | Starboard bow view on No. 8 slip, South Yard, prior to launch, with spectators and launch party on platform. | |
| H812 | 7 November 1903 | Port bow ¾ profile on slip prior to launch, with drag chains in foreground. | |
| H813 | 7 November 1903 | Launch; starboard stern view entering water. | |
| H814 | 7 November 1903 | Starboard bow ¾ profile afloat in Abercorn Basin immediately after launch. | |
| H815 | 7 November 1903 | As above, but more distant view. | |
| H850 | 1 June 1904 | Starboard bow ¾ profile, anchored in Belfast Lough. | |
| H851-852 | 1 June 1904 | Starboard profile in Belfast Lough. | |
| H853 | 1 June 1904 | Starboard bow ¾ profile, anchored in Belfast Lough. | |
| H854 | 1 June 1904 | View forward along starboard boat deck towards bridge, while at sea. | |
| H855 | June 1904 | Dining saloon. | |
| H856 | June 1904 | Library and writing room. | |
| H857 | June 1904 | Similar to above, but plate damaged. | |
| H858-859A | June 1904 | Reception room. | |
| H860 | June 1904 | Corner of reception room. | |

| SHIP NO: 361 | | NAME: DUNLUCE CASTLE |
|---|---|---|
| TYPE: | TONNAGE: | LAUNCH: |
| Passenger Ship | 8113 | 31 March 1904 |
| DELIVERY: | OWNER: | |
| 15 September 1904 | Union-Castle Mail Steamship Company | |

| REF. NO. | DATE | MAIN SUBJECT |
|---|---|---|
| H797 | 31 March 1904 | Forward end of launch cradle, sliding ways, groundways, and drag chains, starboard bow. |
| H798 | 31 March 1904 | Launch party on platform, bottle breaking on port bow, No. 7 slip South Yard. |
| H799 | 31 March 1904 | Starboard bow ¾ profile, afloat in Abercorn Basin after launch. |

| SHIP NO: 363 | | NAME: PARDO |
|---|---|---|
| TYPE: | TONNAGE: | LAUNCH: |
| Cargo Ship | 4365 | 30 June 1904 |
| DELIVERY: | OWNER: | |
| 1 October 1904 | Royal Mail Steam Packet Company | |

| REF. NO. | DATE | MAIN SUBJECT |
|---|---|---|
| H835 | September 1904 | Port stern ¾ profile of completed ship alongside North Yard jetty with Workman Clark's Victoria Yard in background. |
| H836 | September 1904 | Port profile as above, with Workman Clark's Victoria Yard in background. |

| SHIP NO: 364 | | NAME: POTARO |
|---|---|---|
| TYPE: | TONNAGE: | LAUNCH: |
| Cargo Ship | 4378 | 10 September 1904 |
| DELIVERY: | OWNER: | |
| 8 December 1904 | Royal Mail Steam Packet Company | |

| REF. NO. | DATE | MAIN SUBJECT |
|---|---|---|
| H883 | 10 September 1904 | Starboard bow view, afloat in Abercorn Basin after launch from No. 9 slip South Yard. |

| SHIP NO: 366 | | NAME: NIEUW AMSTERDAM |
|---|---|---|
| TYPE:<br>Passenger Ship | TONNAGE:<br>16913 | LAUNCH:<br>28 September 1905 |
| DELIVERY:<br>22 February 1906 | | OWNER:<br>Holland-America Line |

| REF. NO. | DATE | MAIN SUBJECT |
|---|---|---|
| H964-965A | September 1905 | Starboard bow view on No. 1 slip, North Yard prior to launch. |
| H966 | September 1905 | Port stern view on slip prior to launch. |
| H967 | 28 September 1905 | Launch; port stern view entering water. |
| H968 | 28 September 1905 | Port bow view afloat immediately after launch. |
| H969 | 28 September 1905 | Port bow ¾ profile as above, but closer to water level. |
| H1010 | February 1906 | View along upper promenade deck of completed ship. |
| H1011 | February 1906 | Promenade deck stern alcove. |
| H1012 | February 1906 | View along first class lower promenade deck. |
| H1013 | February 1906 | View forward along port first class boat deck towards funnel and bridge. |
| H1014-1015 | February 1906 | First class drawing room, including fireplace and grand piano. |
| H1016-1017 | February 1906 | First class smoke room. |
| H1018 | February 1906 | First class smoke room, area around fireplace. |
| H1019-1020 | February 1906 | First class ladies tea room, including fireplace. |
| H1021 | February 1906 | First class cabin. |
| H1022 | February 1906 | First class enquiries desk and office. |
| H1023 | February 1906 | Second class state room. |
| H1024 | February 1906 | Second class ladies room. |
| H1025 | February 1906 | Second class smoke room. |
| H1026 | February 1906 | Second class dining saloon. |
| H1027 | February 1906 | Third class smoke room. |
| H1028 | February 1906 | View forward from second class after boat deck to first class boat deck, portside. |
| H1029 | February 1906 | View forward from second class after promenade deck to first class promenade deck portside. |
| H1030 | February 1906 | Engine room and telegraphs. |
| H1031 | February 1906 | Purser's office and safe deposit. |
| H1032 | February 1906 | View forward along second class lower promenade deck portside. |
| H1033 | February 1906 | Third class cabin. |
| H1034 | February 1906 | Third class dining saloon. |
| H1035 | February 1906 | Third class pantry. |
| H1036-1037 | February 1906 | Second class dining saloon. |

| SHIP NO: 367 | | NAME: ARAGON |
|---|---|---|
| TYPE:<br>Passenger Ship | TONNAGE:<br>9441 | LAUNCH:<br>23 February 1904 |
| DELIVERY:<br>22 June 1905 | | OWNER:<br>Royal Mail Steam Packet Company |

| REF. NO. | DATE | MAIN SUBJECT |
|---|---|---|
| H884 | February 1904 | Starboard bow ¾ profile on No. 7 slip South Yard prior to launch. |
| H884A | 23 February 1904 | Launch party on platform, breaking bottle on port bow. |
| H885 | February 1904 | Stern view on slip prior to launch. |
| H886 | 23 February 1904 | Launch; starboard stern ¾ profile entering water. |
| H887 | 23 February 1904 | After launch view from platform down empty slip towards hull in water. |
| H888 | 23 February 1904 | Starboard profile in Abercorn Basin after launch. |
| H897 | June 1905 | Starboard bow ¾ profile of completed ship alongside outfitting jetty, South Yard. |
| H899 | June 1905 | Completed stokehold. |
| H900 | June 1905 | Completed engine room looking down on cylinder heads of port and starboard engines. |
| H901 | June 1905 | Laundry and equipment. |
| H902 | June 1905 | Bathroom |
| H903 | June 1905 | View aft along lower starboard promenade deck, with three figures. |
| H904 | June 1905 | View forward over forecastle deck from bridge, while at jetty. |
| H905 | June 1905 | Second class library and writing room. |
| H906 | June 1905 | Hairdressing saloon/barber's shop. |
| H907 | June 1905 | Second class cabin. |
| H908 | June 1905 | Second class dining saloon. |
| H909 | June 1905 | Second class smoke room. |
| H910 | June 1905 | Third class dining saloon. |
| H911 | June 1905 | Third class dining tables on B deck. |
| H912 | June 1905 | Third class cabin. |
| H913 | June 1905 | The children's saloon or nursery, first class. |
| H913-914 | June 1905 | Views forward along starboard first class promenade A deck, with figures. |
| H915 | June 1905 | First class passageway and stairway aft. |
| H916 | June 1905 | View aft from island bridge to passenger superstructure, promenade decks and funnel at sea. |

| SHIP NO: 367 | | NAME: ARAGON |
|---|---|---|
| REF. NO. | DATE | MAIN SUBJECT |
| H917 | June 1905 | Gymnasium equipment at forward end of upper deck. |
| H918 | June 1905 | First class 'bibby' cabin. |
| H919 | June 1905 | First class double cabin. |
| H920-920A | June 1905 | Port near profile of completed ship in Belfast Lough. |
| H921 | June 1905 | Port bow ¾ profile of completed ship in Belfast Lough. |
| H922 | June 1905 | Port profile as above. |
| H924 | June 1905 | First class outer single cabin. |
| H925 | June 1905 | Verandah of first class smoke room at after end of boat deck. |
| H926 | June 1905 | First class smoke room. |
| H927 | June 1905 | Purser's office. |
| H928 | June 1905 | Second class stairway, landing and doorway to boat deck. |
| H929 | June 1905 | View aft over third class deck and poop deck from second class promenade deck at sea. |
| H930 | June 1905 | Pantry, probably second class. |
| H931 | June 1905 | First class outer cabin on deck B.7. |
| H932 | June 1905 | First class dining saloon with decorated table (damaged). |
| H933 | June 1905 | First class dining saloon, after end. |
| H934 | June 1905 | First class dining saloon staircase. |
| H935-935A | June 1905 | First class entrance and staircase. |
| H936 | June 1905 | Corner of sitting room of a first class cabine de luxe. |
| H937 | June 1905 | First class cabine de luxe, sitting room leading to double state room. |
| H938 | June 1905 | Double state room in above cabine de luxe. |
| H939 | June 1905 | First class single state room. |
| H940 | June 1905 | First class social hall/music gallery with seated figures and grand piano. |
| H941 | June 1905 | First class social hall/music gallery with five uniformed musicians. |
| H942 | June 1905 | Upper part of first class staircase. |
| H943 | June 1905 | First class dining saloon sideboard and adjacent entrance door. |
| H944 | June 1905 | Sitting room of a first class cabine de luxe. |
| H944A | June 1905 | Corner of a sitting room of a first class cabine de luxe. |
| H2285-2285A | June 1905 | Starboard profile of cased builder's model. |
| H2286-2286A | June 1905 | As above. |
| H2287 | June 1905 | As above. |

| SHIP NO: 372 | | NAME: AMAZON |
|---|---|---|
| TYPE: Passenger Ship | TONNAGE: 10036 | LAUNCH: 24 February 1906 |
| DELIVERY: 5 June 1906 | | OWNER: Royal Mail Steam Packet Company |
| REF. NO. | DATE | MAIN SUBJECT |
| H1041 | 24 February 1906 | Starboard bow view on No. 6 slip, South Yard, prior to launch. |
| H1042 | 24 February 1906 | Starboard stern view on slip prior to launch. |
| H1043 | 24 February 1906 | Starboard bow ¾ profile afloat in Abercorn Basin immediately after launch. |
| H1043A | 24 February 1906 | Launch party on platform raising hats and with broken bottle on port bow. |
| H1045 | June 1906 | Port bow ¾ profile of completed ship at sea. |
| H1045A | June 1906 | Port bow near profile of completed ship at sea. |
| H1046 | June 1906 | View aft from forward end of starboard boat deck. |
| H1047 | June 1906 | As above, but from position abaft funnel. |
| H1048 | June 1906 | First class dining saloon. |
| H1049 | June 1906 | Ornate sideboard, clock and panelling in first class dining saloon. |
| H1050-1051 | June 1906 | First class balcony smoke room, with figures. |
| H1052 | June 1906 | Combined view of balcony smoke room and lower first class smoke room. |
| H1053 | June 1906 | Adam-style sitting room of first class cabine de luxe. |
| H1054 | June 1906 | Adam-style stateroom of above first class cabine de lux. |
| H1055 | June 1906 | First class double state room and view of others across passageway. |
| H1056-1057 | June 1906 | First class double state room No. 6. |
| H1058 | June 1906 | First class state room with open door leading to bathroom. |
| H1059 | June 1906 | First class inter-connected cabins. |
| H1060 | June 1906 | Verandah of first class smoke room at after end of boat deck. |
| H1061 | June 1906 | First class lower smoke room, with posed figures wearing caps. |
| H1062 | June 1906 | Galley in use, with two cooks. |
| H1063 | June 1906 | Second class dining saloon, with piano. |

| SHIP NO: 377 | | NAME: ORONSA |
|---|---|---|
| TYPE: | TONNAGE: | LAUNCH: |
| Passenger Ship | 7907 | 24 May 1906 |
| DELIVERY: | | OWNER: |
| 16 August 1906 | | Pacific Steam Navigation Company |

| REF. NO. | DATE | MAIN SUBJECT |
|---|---|---|
| H2302-2302A | c.August 1906 | Builder's half model, starboard side. |

| SHIP NO: 382 | | NAME: AVON |
|---|---|---|
| TYPE: | TONNAGE: | LAUNCH: |
| Passenger Ship | 11072 | 2 March 1907 |
| DELIVERY: | | OWNER: |
| 15 June 1907 | | Royal Mail Steam Packet Company |

| REF. NO. | DATE | MAIN SUBJECT |
|---|---|---|
| H1128 | 2 March 1907 | Launch party on platform with bottle breaking on port bow. |
| H1129 | 2 March 1907 | Starboard stern view on No. 6 slip, South Yard prior to launch. |
| H1130 | 2 March 1907 | Starboard bow view on slip prior to launch. |
| H1131 | 2 March 1907 | Port stern view afloat in Abercorn Basin after launch. Includes tug and No. 6 ferry. |
| H1132-1132A | June 1907 | Starboard profile of completed vessel steaming in Belfast Lough. |
| H1133 | June 1907 | View aft along port boat deck and upper awning deck towards funnel. |
| H1134 | June 1907 | View aft from bridge towards funnel, including port and starboard boat decks. |
| H1135 | June 1907 | First class entrance hall, including reception desk and staircase. |
| H1136 | June 1907 | First class social hall, looking forward. |
| H1137 | June 1907 | First class social hall, looking aft. |
| H1138 | June 1907 | First class balcony smoke room. |
| H1139 | June 1907 | First class balcony smoke room and staircase leading to lower smoke room. |
| H1140 | June 1907 | First class lower smoke room. |
| H1141 | June 1907 | Sitting room of first class cabine de luxe. |
| H1142 | June 1907 | Sitting room of first class cabine de luxe, different style to above. |
| H1143 | June 1907 | Double stateroom of first class cabine de luxe. |
| H1144-1145 | June 1907 | First class dining saloon. |
| H1146 | June 1907 | Second class dining saloon. |
| H1147 | June 1907 | Second class library and writing room. |
| H1148 | June 1907 | Second class smoke room. |
| H1149 | June 1907 | First class oak panelled state room. |
| H1150 | June 1907 | First class single cabin. |
| H1151 | June 1907 | First class double cabin. |
| H1152 | June 1907 | First class 'bibby' cabin. |
| H1153 | June 1907 | Purser's office. |
| H1154 | June 1907 | Second class double cabin. |
| H1155 | June 1907 | Starboard upper promenade deck, view aft at sea. |
| H1156 | June 1907 | Starboard upper promenade deck, view forward at sea. |
| H2288 | 5 June 1907 | Starboard profile of cased builder's model. |

| SHIP NO: 385 | | NAME: IROQUOIS |
|---|---|---|

| TYPE: | TONNAGE: | LAUNCH: |
|---|---|---|
| Oil Tanker | 9201 | 27 June 1907 |

| DELIVERY: | OWNER: |
|---|---|
| 19 October 1907 | Anglo-American Oil Company |

| REF. NO. | DATE | MAIN SUBJECT |
|---|---|---|
| H1064 | c.May 1906 | Hydraulic riveting of keel and centre-plate on No. 2 slip, North Yard. |
| H1065 | c.May 1906 | Elevated view of laid keel and centre plate on slip. |
| H1066 | c.May 1906 | Close-up of keel, centre-plate and keel blocks at top of slip. |
| H1067 | c.May 1906 | View of keel and centre-plate from lower end of slip. |
| H1068 | c.June 1906 | Close-up of keel, centre-plate and initial bottom plates. |
| H1069 | c.June 1906 | View of keel, centre-plate and initial bottom plates from lower end of slip. |
| H1070 | c.June 1906 | View along keel plates towards stern, showing combined bottoming and framing arrangement. |
| H1071 | c.June 1906 | As above, but much closer. |
| H1072 | c.June 1906 | View from water side of slip showing stern frames in position. |
| H1073-1076 | c.September 1906 | Men working on internal construction of hull, showing tank subdivision. |
| H1077 | c.October 1906 | Upper deck looking aft, vessel still in frame. |
| H1078 | c.October 1906 | Internal view showing initial laying of plates on tank top/main deck beams. |
| H1079 | c.November 1906 | Upper deck, looking forward, with initial steel deck plate in foreground. |
| H1080 | c.December 1906 | Shell plating starboard side of hull. |
| H1081 | c.January 1907 | Upper deck, looking aft, beginning deck plating and erection of coamings. |
| H1082 | c.January 1907 | Internal constructional view. |
| H1083 | c.February 1907 | Upper deck looking aft, partially plated and coamings in position. |
| H1084 | c.February 1907 | Shell plating starboard side, view forward. |
| H1085 | c. March 1907 | Work on upper deck looking forward from poop deck towards midship bridge structure. |
| H1086 | c.March 1907 | Work on upper deck, looking aft from forecastle deck towards midship bridge structure. |
| H1087 | 27 June 1907 | Port bow view on slip prior to launch, with platform in position. |
| H1087A | 27 June 1907 | Launch party on platform with bottle breaking on port bow. |

| SHIP NO: 385 | | NAME: IROQUOIS |
|---|---|---|

| REF. NO. | DATE | MAIN SUBJECT |
|---|---|---|
| H1088 | 27 June 1907 | Bow view afloat in water and almost alongside North Yard jetty after launch. |
| H1088A | 27 June 1907 | Port bow view alongside North Yard jetty after launch. |
| H1089 | c.October 1907 | Starboard bow ¾ profile of almost completed ship alongside No. 2 outfitting jetty, South Yard. |
| H1103 | c.September 1907 | Starboard side view during outfitting at North Yard and held away from jetty by scows. |
| H1109 | c.September 1907 | Port stern ¾ profile outfitting at North Yard jetty with Workman Clark's Victoria Yard in background. |
| H1110 | October 1907 | Port profile of completed ship as above. |
| H1112 | October 1907 | Port stern ¾ profile of completed ship as above. |

| SHIP NO: 388 | | NAME: ASTURIAS | |
|---|---|---|---|
| TYPE: | TONNAGE: | | LAUNCH: |
| Passenger Ship | 12001 | | 26 September 1907 |
| DELIVERY: | | OWNER: | |
| 8 January 1908 | | Royal Mail Steam Packet Company | |

| REF. NO. | DATE | MAIN SUBJECT |
|---|---|---|
| H1200 | 26 September 1907 | Port bow ¾ profile on No. 8 slip, South Yard prior to launch. |
| H1201 | 26 September 1907 | Port stern view on slip prior to launch. |
| H1202 | 26 September 1907 | Launch; port stern view entering water. |
| H1203 | 26 September 1907 | Starboard near profile afloat in Abercorn Basin after launch. |
| H1204 | January 1908 | View aft from raised awning deck towards funnel and along port boat deck. |
| H1205 | January 1908 | View aft from island bridge towards funnel and passenger superstructure, including boat decks. |
| H1206 | January 1908 | View aft along starboard upper promenade deck. |
| H1207 | January 1908 | View forward along port upper promenade deck. |
| H1208 | January 1908 | First class entrance hall, including enquiries office and staircase. |
| H1209-1210 | January 1908 | First class social hall, including lift, piano and writing desks. |
| H1211 | January 1908 | First class balcony smoke room and lower smoke room. |
| H1212 | January 1908 | First class lower smoke room and staircase. |
| H1213-1214 | January 1908 | First class dining saloon. |
| H1215 | January 1908 | Sitting room of first class cabine de luxe. |
| H1216 | January 1908 | Sitting room as above, but decorated in a different style. |
| H1217 | January 1908 | Purser's office. |
| H1218 | January 1908 | Galley, with posed figures in background. |
| H1219 | January 1908 | First class outer double cabin. |
| H1251 | January 1908 | First class cabin (upright format). |
| H1252 | January 1908 | Portside view of after end of first and second class promenade decks and boat deck. |

| SHIP NO: 389 | | NAME: NAVAHOE | |
|---|---|---|---|
| TYPE: | TONNAGE: | | LAUNCH: |
| Sailing Oil Barge | 7718 | | 10 October 1907 |
| DELIVERY: | | OWNER: | |
| 18 January 1908 | | Anglo-American Oil Company | |

| REF. NO. | DATE | MAIN SUBJECT |
|---|---|---|
| H1090-1092 | c.October 1906 | Views of laid keel and erected centre plate on No. 5 slip, South Yard. |
| H1093 + H1116A | c.December 1906 | View along keel and centre plates towards stern, showing combined bottoming and framing arrangements. |
| H1094-1096R + H1116A | c.February 1907 | Progress on internal framing and constructional arrangements, showing tank subdivisions. |
| H1097-1098 | c.March 1907 | Internal views showing initial laying of plates on tank-top/main-deck beams. |
| H1099 | c.May 1907 | Upper deck aft from partially plated forecastle deck, over coaming and deck beams to poop deck. |
| H1100 | c.May 1907 | Upper deck view forward from after end of starboard coaming, over deck beams to forecastle deck. |
| H1101 | c.June 1907 | Upper deck view forward from partially plated poop deck to plated forecastle deck. |
| H1102 | c.June 1907 | Internal view along plated tank top/main deck below upper deck. |
| H1104 | c.July 1907 | Upper deck view forward from capstan on poop deck, deck plating not completed. |
| H1105 | 10 October 1907 | Starboard bow view on slip prior to launch. |
| H1106 | 10 October 1907 | Starboard stern view on slip prior to launch. |
| H1106A | 10 October 1907 | Starboard stern ¾ profile on slip prior to launch; elevated view includes gantry and adjacent slip. |
| H1107 | 10 October 1907 | Launch; starboard stern profile entering water. |
| H1108 | 10 October 1907 | Starboard bow ¾ profile off Queen's Quay in Victoria Channel after launch. |
| H1111 | c.August 1907 | Upper deck view aft from forecastle deck, tank top and deck plating almost completed. |
| H1113 | c.December 1907 | Starboard bow view of almost completed vessel at No. 1 outfitting jetty, South Yard. |
| H1114 | c.November 1907 | Upper deck view forward from poop deck during outfitting. |
| H1115 | c.November 1907 | Upper deck view aft from break of forecastle deck during outfitting. |
| H1116 | c.January 1908 | Starboard bow ¾ profile of completed 6-masted schooner-rigged vessel, built for towing by IROQUOIS (385). |

| SHIP NO: 390 | | NAME: ROTTERDAM | |
|---|---|---|---|

| TYPE: | TONNAGE: | LAUNCH: |
|---|---|---|
| Passenger Ship | 23980 | 3 March 1908 |

| DELIVERY: | OWNER: |
|---|---|
| 3 June 1908 | Holland-America Line |

| REF. NO. | DATE | MAIN SUBJECT |
|---|---|---|
| H1157 | June 1907 | Port bow view in frame on No. 3 slip, North Yard. |
| H1158-1158A | November 1907 | Port bow view on slip with shell plating completed. |
| H1159 | November 1907 | Starboard stern profile on slip, with shell plating completed. |
| H1161&1162A | March 1907 | Starboard profile on slip prior to launch, view across Victoria Channel. |
| H1162 | March 1907 | Port bow view on slip prior to launch. |
| H1163 | March 1907 | Bow view on slip prior to launch. |
| H1164-1164A | March 1907 | Port stern view on slip prior to launch. |
| H1165 | 3 March 1907 | Launch; port stern view entering water. |
| H1166 | 3 March 1907 | Starboard bow ¾ profile alongside jetty after launch. |
| H1224 | November 1907 | Port bow view on slip with shell plating completed, during reconstruction of No. 2 slip. |
| H1265 | June 1908 | First class dining saloon, with balcony. |
| H1266 | June 1908 | First class balcony and smoke room including dome. |
| H1267-1267A | June 1908 | First class lower smoke room, including fireplace. |
| H1268 | June 1908 | Second class smoke room with seated posed figures drinking. |
| H1269 | June 1908 | First class balcony smoke room, with staircase leading to lower smoke room. |
| H1270 | June 1908 | View forward along portside enclosed upper promenade deck, including wicker chairs and single figure. |
| H1271 | June 1908 | View from starboard bridge wing over boat deck and towards funnels. |
| H1273 | June 1908 | View forward towards end of portside enclosed upper promenade deck, with single figure. |
| H1274 | June 1908 | View aft along starboard open promenade deck. |
| H1275-1276 | June 1908 | First class social hall, including grand piano and fireplace. |
| H1277-1278 | June 1908 | First class palm court, with dome and wicker furniture. |
| H1279 | June 1908 | First class palm court staircase, landing and dome. |
| H1280-1281 | June 1908 | First class library and writing room, with dome and fireplace. |
| H1282 | June 1908 | First class staircase from social hall landing to palm court landing above. |

| SHIP NO: 390 | | NAME: ROTTERDAM | |
|---|---|---|---|

| REF. NO. | DATE | MAIN SUBJECT |
|---|---|---|
| H1284 | June 1908 | State room and adjoining sitting room of first class suite. |
| H1285 | June 1908 | Balcony and well of first class dining saloon. |
| H1287 | June 1908 | First class hairdressing salon. |
| H1288-1294 | June 1908 | First class four and two berth cabins, including one with private bathroom (H1291). |
| H1299-1299A | June 1908 | Second class dining saloon. |
| H1300 | June 1908 | Second class smoke room with mast passing through floor to ceiling. |
| H1301 | June 1908 | Second class library and writing room with mast passing through floor to ceiling. |
| H1303 | June 1908 | Galley. |
| H1304 | June 1908 | First class pantry. |
| H1305 | June 1908 | Third class open space lower deck with companionways and side seats. |
| H1306 | June 1908 | Third class general room with wooden slat seats. |
| H1307 | June 1908 | Second class four berth cabin. |
| H1310 | June 1908 | Starboard bow ¾ profile of completed ship in Belfast Lough. |
| H1311 | June 1908 | Starboard stern ¾ profile as above. |
| H1312 | June 1908 | Third class dining saloon. |
| H1313 | June 1908 | Third class six berth cabin. |
| H2352-2352A | 2 March 1908 | Cased builder's No. 2 model, starboard profile and near profile. |
| H2353 | 1 December 1907 | Cased builder's No. 1 model, starboard bow ¾ profile. |

84

| SHIP NO: 392 | | NAME: PERICLES | |
|---|---|---|---|
| TYPE: | TONNAGE: | | LAUNCH: |
| Passenger Ship | 10924 | | 21 December 1907 |
| DELIVERY: | | OWNER: | |
| 4 June 1908 | | George Thompson & Company | |

| REF. NO. | DATE | MAIN SUBJECT |
|---|---|---|
| H1178 | c.September 1907 | Port bow view on No. 4 slip, North Yard, shell plating in progress. |
| H1179 | c.September 1907 | View aft from partly plated forecastle deck to partly constructed bridge. |
| H1180 | c.October 1907 | Starboard stern view on slip, shell plating almost completed. |
| H1181 | c.October 1907 | Partly laid wooden planking on foredeck, hatchways and partly constructed island bridge. |
| H1182 | 21December 1907 | Port bow view on slip prior to launch. |
| H1183 | 21 December 1907 | Starboard stern view on slip prior to launch. |
| H1184 | 21 December 1907 | Distant starboard bow view afloat immediately after launch. |
| H1186 | June 1908 | View along upper promenade deck. |
| H1187 | June 1908 | View forward along port boat deck. |
| H1188-1189 | June 1908 | First class staircase and landing. |
| H1190-1191 | June 1908 | First class library and writing room. |
| H1192-1193 | June 1908 | First class dining saloon. |
| H1194 | June 1908 | First class panelled double stateroom. |
| H1195-1197 | June 1908 | First class cabins. |
| H1198 | June 1908 | Third class dining saloon. |
| H1199 | June 1908 | Third class four berth cabin. |
| H1253 | June 1908 | First class smoke room, with mast passing through floor to ceiling. |
| H1254 | June 1908 | Starboard stern ¾ profile of completed ship moving down Victoria Channel. |
| H1255 | June 1908 | Third class smoke room. |
| H1256 | June 1908 | Third class two berth outer cabin. |
| H1257 | June 1908 | First class cabin. |
| H1258 | June 1908 | Starboard bow ¾ profile of completed ship alongside No. 1 outfitting jetty, Abercorn Basin. |
| H1259 | June 1908 | Starboard stern ¾ profile of completed ship as above. |
| H1260 | June 1908 | Third class dining saloon, with tables laid and decorated with plants. |
| H1261-1261A | June 1908 | Third class smoke room with mast passing through floor to ceiling. |

| SHIP NO: 392 | | NAME: PERICLES |
|---|---|---|
| REF. NO. | DATE | MAIN SUBJECT |
| H1262 | June 1908 | Third class smoke room with piano and decorative plants. |
| H1264 | June 1908 | First class dining saloon. |
| H2332 | June 1908 | Starboard profile of cased builder's model. |
| H2335 | 4 June 1908 | Starboard bow ¾ profile of completed ship under tow in Victoria Channel. |

| SHIP NO: 393 | | NAME: LAPLAND | |
|---|---|---|---|
| TYPE: | TONNAGE: | | LAUNCH: |
| Passenger Ship | 18565 | | 27 June 1908 |
| DELIVERY: | | OWNER: | |
| 27 March 1909 | | Red Star Line | |

| REF. NO. | DATE | MAIN SUBJECT |
|---|---|---|
| H1222 | c.September 1907 | Starboard bow ¾ profile in frame, on No. 1 slip North Yard, during reconstruction of No. 2 slip. |
| H1226 | c.September 1907 | As above but slightly earlier date. |
| H1233 | c.June 1908 | Port side view of hull looking forward, prior to launch, during reconstruction of slips 2–3. |
| H1316 | June 1908 | Starboard bow view on slip during preparations for launch. |
| H1317 | June 1908 | Port stern view on slip prior to launch. |
| H1318 | 27 June 1908 | Launch; port stern view entering water. |
| H1319 | 27 June 1908 | Port bow view afloat immediately after launch. |
| H1320 | c.March 1909 | Port side near profile at jetty in final stages of outfitting. |
| H1321 | c.March 1909 | Port stern ¾ profile as above. |
| H1322 | c.March 1909 | Port bow view alongside jetty in final stages of outfitting. |
| H1703 | c.1907 | Tinted, and probably coloured, rigging plan $\frac{1}{16}$" = 1 ft) as built. |
| H1704 | c.1907 | Alternative 'B' rigging plan showing three funnels and different profile. |

| SHIP NO: 394 | NAME: LAURENTIC (ALBERTA) | |
|---|---|---|
| TYPE: | TONNAGE: | LAUNCH: |
| Passenger Ship | 14892 | 10 September 1908 |
| DELIVERY: | OWNER: | |
| 15 April 1909 | Oceanic Steam Navigation Company (White Star Line) (Order placed by Dominion Line) | |

| REF. NO. | DATE | MAIN SUBJECT |
|---|---|---|
| H1340 | 10 September 1908 | Starboard bow view on No. 6 slip, South Yard prior to launch. |
| H1341 | 10 September 1908 | Starboard stern view on slip prior to launch. |
| H1342 | 10 September 1908 | Starboard view of rudder and triple screw arrangement, prior to launch. |
| H1343 | 10 September 1908 | Starboard stern ¾ profile on slip prior to launch. |
| H1344 | 10 September 1908 | Launch; starboard stern view entering water. |
| H1345 | 10 September 1908 | Port stern ¾ profile afloat after launch. |
| H1348 | 15 April 1909 | Starboard bow ¾ profile of completed ship in Belfast Lough. |
| H1349 | 15 April 1909 | Similar to above, but including men at stern of tug in foreground. |
| H1350 | 15 April 1909 | Starboard profile of completed ship in Belfast Lough. |
| H1352 | April 1909 | Second class smoke room. |
| H1353 | April 1909 | Second class library and writing room, with mast passing through floor to ceiling. |
| H1354 | April 1909 | First class two berth cabin. |
| H1355 | April 1909 | Second class dining saloon. |
| H1356 | April 1909 | Third class general room. |
| H1357 | April 1909 | First class four berth cabin. |
| H1358 | April 1909 | Third class dining saloon. |
| H1359 | April 1909 | Second class four berth cabin. |
| H2325A | September 1908 | Starboard stern view on slip prior to launch, including vessels on adjacent slips. |
| H2550-2555 | 3&10 November 1908 | Engine bed and funnel being lifted on board by combination of floating crane and sheer-legs. |

| SHIP NO: 397 | NAME: MINNEWASKA | |
|---|---|---|
| TYPE: | TONNAGE: | LAUNCH: |
| Passenger Ship | 14816 | 12 November 1908 |
| DELIVERY: | OWNER: | |
| 24 April 1909 | Atlantic Transport Company | |

| REF. NO. | DATE | MAIN SUBJECT |
|---|---|---|
| H1360 | April 1909 | Port bow ¾ profile of completed ship alongside No. 1 outfitting jetty, South Yard. |
| H1361 | April 1909 | As above, but more distant and nearer to profile view. |
| H2556-2558 | 18 November 1908 | Floating crane lifting boiler and mast on board during outfitting. |

| SHIP NO: 399 | NAME: MEGANTIC | |
|---|---|---|
| TYPE: | TONNAGE: | LAUNCH: |
| Passenger Ship | 14877 | 10 December 1908 |
| DELIVERY: | OWNER: | |
| 3 June 1909 | Oceanic Steam Navigation Company (White Star Line) | |

| REF. NO. | DATE | MAIN SUBJECT |
|---|---|---|
| H1346 | December 1908 | Starboard bow profile on No. 7 slip, South Yard prior to launch. |
| H1346A | June 1909 | Port near profile of completed ship alongside No. 1 outfitting jetty, South Yard. |
| H1347 | December 1908 | Starboard stern view on slip prior to launch. |
| H2559-2562 | 6 January 1909 | Floating crane lifting boilers on board during outfitting. |
| H2563 | c.6 January 1909 | Machinery and shafting on deck of floating crane for lifting on board. |
| H2564-2567 | 20&29 January 1909 | Starboard stern view with floating crane lifting masts on board. |

| SHIP NO: 400 | | NAME: OLYMPIC | |
|---|---|---|---|
| **TYPE:** | | **TONNAGE:** | **LAUNCH:** |
| Passenger Ship | | 45324 | 20 October 1910 |
| **DELIVERY:** | | **OWNER:** | |
| 31 May 1911 | | Oceanic Steam Navigation Company (White Star Line) | |

| REF. NO. | DATE | MAIN SUBJECT |
|---|---|---|
| H1220-1250<br>+ H1324<br>+ H2518-2549<br>+ H2518-2549<br>+ H2568-2617 | 1907-1908 | Reconstruction of North Yard slips 2&3 and erection of Arrol gantry for building OLYMPIC & TITANIC (400&401) |
| H1323&1325 | c.December 1908 | Keel blocks for OLYMPIC on No. 2 slip with work on No. 3 slip in progress. General view of slips and gantry from top end. |
| H1326 | 1 January 1909 | General view of slips 2&3 from lower end, with OLYMPIC'S keel laid on No. 2 slip. |
| H1328 | 18 February 1909 | Centre plate and beginning work on tank floors aft, viewed from lower end of slip. |
| 1329 | 18 February 1909 | Hydraulic riveting of centre plate, including riveters and portable furnace. |
| H1330-1331 | 8 May 1909 | Fore and aft views of double bottom, and initial plating of tank top. |
| H1332-1333 | 30 July 1909 | Plating tank top with erected aft end frames in background. |
| H1429 | May 1911 | First class single berth stateroom. |
| H1440 | October 1910 | Port bow view on slip prior to launch, with TITANIC (401) shell plated on No. 3 slip. |
| H1441 | October 1910 | Portside view of forward launching cradle and underside of port bow and hull. |
| H1447 | October 1910 | Hydraulic launching trigger. |
| H1448 | October 1910 | Port bow view on No. 2 slip prior to launch. |
| H1449 | October 1910 | 15½ ton anchor on horse-drawn Harkness wagon for moving to ship. |
| H1453 | 20 October 1910 | Launch; port stern view of light grey painted hull entering water. |
| H1454 | c.October 1910 | Starboard stern ¾ profile alongside Alexandra Wharf after launch. |
| H1455 | c.November 1910 | Two rows of completed boilers in Engine Works boiler shop. |
| H1456 | c.November 1910 | After end view of starboard main engine nearly completed in Engine Works erecting shop. |
| H1457 | c.November 1910 | Turbine-driven centre propeller in Engine Works. |

| SHIP NO: 400 | | NAME: OLYMPIC |
|---|---|---|

| REF. NO. | DATE | MAIN SUBJECT |
|---|---|---|
| H1458 | c.November 1910 | One of the main condensers with casing partly removed, in Engine Works. |
| H1459 | c.November 1910 | Casing of one of the change-over valves in Engine Works, with figure. |
| H1461 | May 1911 | Bay window and corner of first class dining saloon. |
| H1469 | October 1910 | Bow view on slip prior to launch, with TITANIC shell plated on No. 3 slip. |
| H1471 | c.December 1910 | Water-tight door in raised open position during outfitting. |
| H1485 | May 1911 | First class two berth stateroom. |
| H1487 | c.December 1910 | Watertight door in lowered closed position during outfitting. |
| H1490 | 1 April 1911 | Port bow view of ship entering Thompson (Era) Graving Dock for final outfitting. |
| H1493 | 1 April 1911 | Starboard bow view of ship preparing to enter Thompson Graving Dock. |
| H1495 | 1 April 1911 | Starboard bow view of ship entering Thompson Graving Dock. |
| H1496 | 1 April 1911 | Bow view of ship entering Thompson Graving Dock. |
| H1498 | 1 April 1911 | Starboard bow ¾ profile of ship at outfitting wharf prior to entering Thompson Graving Dock. |
| H1500 | April 1911 | View aft along port hull from side of graving dock showing arrangement of timber shoring. |
| H1501 | April 1911 | View forward as above. |
| H1502 | April 1911 | View aft as above, but including lifeboats and funnels. |
| H1504 | April 1911 | View of hull underside and shores above from dock floor. |
| H1505 | April 1911 | Hull underside and damage to keel blocks from dock floor. |
| H1506 | April 1911 | Underside bow view from dock floor. |
| H1507 | April 1911 | View of hull underside and shores above, from dock floor. |
| H1508 | April 1911 | View forward from after end of starboard boat deck during outfitting. |
| H1509 | c.May 1911 | Row of wash basins in public W.C., probably first class. |
| H1510 | April 1911 | Turbine propeller and two propeller bosses on wharf side with floating crane in background. |
| H1511 | April 1911 | Triple propeller arrangement and rudder, portside view from dock floor, with three figures. |
| H1512 | April 1911 | Port propeller, centre propeller, posed workers and caisson from dock floor. |
| H1513 | April 1911 | Triple propeller arrangement, rudder and underside of counter from port side of graving dock. |

| SHIP NO: 400 | | NAME: OLYMPIC |
|---|---|---|
| REF. NO. | DATE | MAIN SUBJECT |
| H1514 | April 1911 | Port stern profile of counter, rudder and centre propeller from side of graving dock. |
| H1515 | April 1911 | Port bow profile from side of graving dock with pump house and chimney in background. |
| H1516-1516A | May 1911 | Workers disembarking from almost completed ship at Thompson deepwater outfitting wharf. |
| H1518 | May 1911 | Promenade deck and windows of first class reading and writing room. |
| H1519 | May 1911 | Promenade deck and windows of first class smoke room, starboard side. |
| H1520 | May 1911 | Promenade deck and windows of first class smoke room, port side. |
| H1521 | May 1911 | Promenade deck and windows of palm court, starboard side. |
| H1522 | May 1911 | Promenade deck and lounge windows, port side. |
| H1523 | May 1911 | Windows of gymnasium at forward end of starboard boat deck. |
| H1524 | May 1911 | View aft from port boat deck towards poop deck, near completion of outfitting. |
| H1525 | May 1911 | Panelling and installed electric heater. |
| H1526-1527 | May 1911 | Port and starboard views of ventilating and heating fans at after end of boat deck during outfitting. |
| H1528 | May 1911 | 10-cwt stores lift and electric motor. |
| H1529 | May 1911 | Panelling and concealed electrical distribution box. |
| H1530 | May 1911 | Wash basin and bath in private bathroom, probably first class. |
| H1531 | May 1911 | Panelling and open door leading to bathroom/W.C., first class. |
| H1532 | May 1911 | Whale-back tube ventilating shaft cover, during outfitting. |
| H1533 | May 1911 | Port main generating set in electric engine room. |
| H1534 | May 1911 | Starboard main generating set in electric engine room, with two figures. |
| H1534A | May 1911 | Transverse section drawing of electric engine room, showing generating sets. |
| H1535 | May 1911 | Main feeder switchboard. |
| H1536 | May 1911 | 2½ ton electric crane on starboard side of poop deck, near completion of outfitting. |
| H1537 | May 1911 | Bath in private bathroom, probably first class. |
| H1539 | 29 May 1911 | Port profile of completed ship at sea. |
| H1539A | 29 May 1911 | As above, but not sharp. |
| H1539B | 29 May 1911 | Port bow near profile of completed ship at sea — more distant view than above. |

| SHIP NO: 400 | | NAME: OLYMPIC |
|---|---|---|
| REF. NO. | DATE | MAIN SUBJECT |
| H1540 | 29 May 1911 | Port bow ¾ profile of completed ship at sea. |
| H1540A | 29 May 1911 | As above, but darker print. |
| H1541 | May 1911 | View aft along starboard upper promenade deck. |
| H1542 | May 1911 | View aft along port upper promenade deck. |
| H1543 | May 1911 | View aft from second funnel along port boat deck. |
| H1544-1545 | May 1911 | First class dining saloon. |
| H1546-1547 | May 1911 | First class lounge. |
| H1548-1549A | May 1911 | First class smoke room. |
| H1550 | May 1911 | First class swimming bath. |
| H1571-1572 | May 1911 | First class reading and writing room. |
| H1573 | May 1911 | First class palm court. |
| H1574 | May 1911 | First class palm court, with open door leading to smoke room. |
| H1575 | May 1911 | First class restaurant. |
| H1576 | May 1911 | First class main staircase, balustrade and bronze figure. |
| H1577 | May 1911 | Landing of first class main staircase, with carved panel incorporating clock and symbol of honour and glory crowning time. |
| H1578 | May 1911 | General view of first class main staircase, including landing, clock and part of dome. |
| H1579 | May 1911 | First class after main staircase, differing in the simpler design of the clock panel. |
| H1580 | May 1911 | View aft along starboard enclosed promenade deck from first class entrance. |
| H1581 | May 1911 | First class gymnasium. |
| H1582 | May 1911 | First class suite bedroom, modern Dutch style — sycamore and inlay. |
| H1583 | May 1911 | First class suite bedroom, modern Dutch style — oak and inlay. |
| H1584 | May 1911 | First class suite bedroom, old Dutch style. |
| H1589 | May 1911 | First class suite bedroom, Queen Anne style. |
| H1586 | May 1911 | First class suite bedroom, modern Dutch style — oak and inlay. |
| H1587 | May 1911 | First class suite bedroom, Italian renaissance style. |
| H1588 | May 1911 | Sitting room of first class parlour suite, Adam style. |
| H1589 | May 1911 | Sitting room of first class parlour suite 1388, Louis XVI style. |
| H1590 | May 1911 | First class suite bedroom, Empire style. |
| H1591 | May 1911 | Sitting room of first class parlour suite, Regency style. |
| H1592 | May 1911 | First class suite bedroom/sitting room, Empire style. |
| H1593 | May 1911 | First class suite bedroom Empire style. |

| SHIP NO: 400 | | NAME: OLYMPIC |
|---|---|---|
| REF. NO. | DATE | MAIN SUBJECT |
| H1594 | May 1911 | Sitting room of first class parlour suite, Adam style. |
| H1595 | May 1911 | Sitting room of first class parlour suite, Regency style. |
| H1596 | May 1911 | First class reading and writing room. |
| H1597 | May 1911 | First class after main staircase, balustrade and electric candelabra. |
| H1598 | May 1911 | Alleyway with overhead piping and trunking leading to passageway. |
| H1606 | May 1911 | Second class reading and writing room/library. |
| H1602 | May 1911 | Second class smoke room. |
| H1603-1603A | May 1911 | First class suite bedroom, Louis XVI style. |
| H1605-1606 | May 1911 | Sitting room of first class parlour suite, Louis XIV style (R Sloan suite). |
| H1607 | October 1911 | HMS HAWKE collision damage — wooden patch at stern covering damage. |
| H1608 | October 1911 | HMS HAWKE collision damage — hole between saloon and upper deck from inside looking aft. |
| H1609 | October 1911 | HMS HAWKE collision damage — hole between saloon and upper deck from inside looking forward. |
| H1610 | October 1911 | HMS HAWKE collision damage — hole from shaft tunnel. |
| H1611 | October 1911 | HMS HAWKE collision damage — boss plating showing temporary wedging in holes. |
| H1612 | October 1911 | HMS HAWKE collision damage — boss plating showing holes open. |
| H1613 | October 1911 | HMS HAWKE collision damage — upper hole, wood covering removed. |
| H1614 | October 1911 | HMS HAWKE collision damage — lower hole, wood covering removed. |
| H1615 | October 1911 | HMS HAWKE collision damage — lower hole from inside. |
| H1616 | October 1911 | HMS HAWKE collision damage — hole in bossing and lower hole, looking forward. |
| H1617 | October 1911 | HMS HAWKE collision damage — hole in bossing and lower hole. |
| H1618 | October 1911 | HMS HAWKE collision damage — starboard propeller looking aft from lower hole. |
| H1619 | October 1911 | HMS HAWKE collision damage — starboard propeller, looking forward from dock floor. |
| H1620 | October 1911 | HMS HAWKE collision damage — starboard propeller blade, looking forward. |
| H1621 | October 1911 | HMS HAWKE collision damage — starboard propeller and holes, looking forward from top of pontoon. |

| SHIP NO: 400 | | NAME: OLYMPIC |
|---|---|---|
| REF. NO. | DATE | MAIN SUBJECT |
| H1622 | October 1911 | HMS HAWKE collision damage — middle hole looking forward, with figure. |
| H1623 | October 1911 | HMS HAWKE collision damage — as above, but different view with two figures. |
| H1624-1624A | October 1911 | HMS HAWKE collision damage — part of upper hole, from inside. |
| H1625 | October 1911 | HMS HAWKE collision damage — part of upper hole, looking forward. |
| H1626 | October 1911 | HMS HAWKE collision damage — damaged starboard propeller blades in shop. |
| H1628 | October 1911 | HMS HAWKE collision damage — damaged plates removed from boss. |
| H1629-1632 | 6 November 1911 | HMS HAWKE collision damage — details of damaged shell plates. |
| H1633 | March 1912 | Starboard bridge wing from wheel house. |
| H1634 | March 1912 | As above, but from outside wheel house. |
| H1635 | March 1912 | Two lifeboats and collapsible lifeboat abaft starboard bridge wing. |
| H1636 | March 1912 | Port bow view in Thompson Graving Dock while under repair. |
| H1637 | March 1912 | Starboard bow view entering Thompson Graving Dock, with starboard bow ¾ profile of TITANIC outfitting. |
| H1653 | March 1912 | Close-up view of centre propeller shaft and two blades, while in Thompson Graving Dock. |
| H1656 | c.May 1911 | View aft to starboard poop deck while swinging and outfitting basin with Thompson Graving Dock and TITANIC in background. |
| H1705 | March 1912 | Bottom of hull from floor of Thompson Graving Dock. |
| H1706 | March 1912 | Bow view entering Thompson Graving Dock with starboard bow view of TITANIC outfitting. |
| H1707 | March 1912 | Centre propeller and port propeller with missing blade, Thompson Graving Dock. |
| H1708 | March 1912 | As above, but different view with posed workers. |
| H1709 | March 1912 | Hull and shores from floor of dock. |
| H1825 | c.December 1912 | Bow view in Thompson Graving Dock, during post-TITANIC disaster refitting. |
| H1826 | c.December 1912 | Deck level view from anchor on forecastle deck, aft to bridge. |
| H1827 | c.December 1912 | View aft to bridge from anchor chain cables on forecastle deck. |
| H1828 | c.December 1912 | Corrosion detail with penny coin for scale — location unknown. |

| REF. NO. | DATE | MAIN SUBJECT |
|---|---|---|
| H1828A-1830 | c.December 1912 | Corrosion detail — location unknown. |
| H1831 | c.December 1912 | Corrosion detail with penny coin for scale — first class upper deck. |
| H1832 | c.December 1912 | Two pieces of corroded steel with penny coin for scale. |
| H1833 | c.December 1912 | Piece of corroded steel with penny coin for scale. |
| H1834-1835 | c.December 1912 | Work in progress in fitting watertight inner shell. |
| H1836 | c.December 1912 | Work in progress in fitting watertight inner shell, with riveters. |
| H1837 | c.December 1912 | As above, at boiler hold, with worker looking through circular hole. |
| H1838-1838A | c.December 1912 | First class Cafe-Parisienne on B deck. |
| H1839 | c.December 1912 | First class restaurant reception room. |
| H1840-1840A | c.December 1912 | First class restaurant. |
| H1841 | c.December 1912 | First class reading and writing room. |

**400 SERIES**

| | | |
|---|---|---|
| H2363 | January 1909 | Work on keel and centre plate viewed from lower end of slip. |
| H2364 | February 1909 | Centre plate and beginning work on tank floors aft, viewed from lower end of slip. |
| H2365 | July 1909 | Plating tank top, but before erection of aft end frames. |
| H2366 | August 1909 | 200 ton floating crane lifting part of sternframe on to slip. |
| H2367 | August 1909 | Positioning port boss arm between after end framing and sternframe. |
| H2368 | 20 August 1909 | Boss arms in position. |
| H2369 | c.August 1909 | Unshipping a boss arm casting. |
| H2370 | c.August 1909 | Frames erected from aft end to midships. |
| H2371 | c.20 November 1909 | Port bow view fully framed with forward tank top of TITANIC on No. 3 slip. |
| H2372 | c.November 1910 | Port intermediate cylinder casting, with figure, in Engine Works shop. |
| H2373 | c.20 November 1909 | Port bow view fully framed. |
| H2374 | 16 August 1909 | Upper and lower parts of stern frame in position. |
| H2375 | c.November 1910 | Wooden pattern for part of turbine casing assembled in pattern shop. |
| H2376 | c.November 1910 | Mock-up of side screen window on B deck with crank handle operating arrangement. |
| H2377 | 6-15 April 1910 | Starboard bow views of TITANIC fully framed with OLYMPIC fully plated alongside. |

| REF. NO. | DATE | MAIN SUBJECT |
|---|---|---|
| H2378 | c.April 1910 | Starboard profile of builder's model, without case, identified on the negative as OLYMPIC and TITANIC, but as OLYMPIC on the model. |
| H2379 | c.April 1910 | Starboard bow ¾ profile as above. |
| H2380 | c.November 1910 | Two examples of different designs of dining saloon chairs, probably third class. |
| H2381 | c.November 1910 | Boiler uptake in Engine Works boiler shop. |
| H2382 | 5 August 1910 | Port bow view on slip with TITANIC partially plated alongside (unsharp). |
| H2383 | c.April 1910 | Starboard bow ¾ profile of builder's half model OLYMPIC/TITANIC on adjustable base. |
| H2384 | c.April 1910 | Starboard stern ¾ profile as above. |
| H2385-2387 | c.April 1910 | Three views of builder's half model OLYMPIC/TITANIC, different to above. |
| H2388 | April 1909 | Fore and aft view from gantry of tank top before plating. |
| H2389 | May 1909 | View of double bottom from lower end of slip, with initial work on plating tank top. |
| H2390 | August 1909 | Boss arms casting on deck of 200 ton floating crane. |
| H2291 | August 1909 | 200 ton floating crane unshipping stern frame. |
| H2392 | August 1909 | 200 ton floating crane lifting part of stern frame on to slip. |
| H2393-2394 | August 1909 | Lower part of stern frame in position with the upper part being set down on slip. |
| H2395 | August 1909 | Upper part of stern frame being lifted into position. |
| H2396 | 16 August 1909 | Upper part of stern frame in position. |
| H2397 | c.17 August 1909 | Beginning operation to lift and position boss arms. |
| H2398 | c.November 1910 | Wooden pattern for part of turbine casing assembled in pattern shop. |
| H2399 | 20 November 1909 | Port bow view of last frame being raised into position. |
| H2400 | c.August 1909 | Rudder head mounted on lathe in Engine Works turning shop. |
| H2401-2402 | c.April 1910 | Starboard near profile and profile of cased builder's model, OLYMPIC/TITANIC with sign 'the largest ships in the world.' |
| H2403 | c.October 1910 | Workers' gangway to port bow for outfitting at deepwater wharf. |
| H2404 | November 1910 | Floating crane lifting a boiler on board during outfitting. |
| H2405 | c.November 1910 | Installation of turbine during outfitting. |
| H2406 | 9 January 1911 | Boat deck looking aft during outfitting, including jib of floating crane. |

| SHIP NO: 400 | | NAME: OLYMPIC |
|---|---|---|
| REF. NO. | DATE | MAIN SUBJECT |
| H2407 | 2 February 1911 | No. 3 funnel ready for shipping on board during outfitting. |
| H2408 | 7 February 1911 | Starboard boat deck looking forward during outfitting. |
| H2409 | 7 February 1911 | Port boat deck looking aft during outfitting. |
| H2410 | c.February 1911 | One set of whistles before installation. |
| H2411 | c.February 1911 | Port boat deck looking aft with two funnels in position. |
| H2412 | 23 March 1911 | Last funnel (No. 4) leaving shop. |
| H2413 | 23 March 1911 | Steam crane towing last funnel (No. 4) to the deepwater outfitting wharf. |
| H2414-2415 | 23 March 1911 | Two views of last funnel (No. 4) alongside ship. |
| H2416 | 23 March 1911 | Last funnel (No. 4) being towed down Queen's Road to the deepwater outfitting wharf. |
| H2417-2417A | March 1911 | Starboard bow ¾ profile during outfitting with four funnels in position. |
| H2418 | 1 April 1911 | Bow view, about to enter Thompson Graving Dock. |
| H2419 | March 1911 | Port bow view at deepwater wharf during outfitting. |
| H2420 | April 1911 | Starboard propeller bossing from floor of dry dock. |
| H2421 | April 1911 | View aft along starboard hull from floor of dry dock. |
| H2422 | 1 April 1911 | Starboard bow view in dry dock from the dock side. |

| SHIP NO: 401 | | NAME: TITANIC | |
|---|---|---|---|
| TYPE: Passenger Ship | TONNAGE: 46328 | | LAUNCH: 31 May 1911 |
| DELIVERY: 2 April 1912 | | OWNER: Oceanic Steam Navigation Company (White Star Line) | |
| REF. NO. | DATE | MAIN SUBJECT | |
| H1330 | c.31 March 1909 | Keel laid on reconstructed No. 3 slip, North Yard, Bottom of OLYMPIC (400) on No. 2 slip in foreground. | |
| H1331-1333 | 8 May- 30 July 1909 | Progress on bottom work, as background to views of work on OLYMPIC on No. 2 slip. | |
| H1440 | October 1910 | Port bow view No. 3 slip, shell plated, with OLYMPIC (400) prepared for launch on No. 2 slip. | |
| H1469 | October 1910 | Port bow view, shell plated, with OLYMPIC prepared for launch on adjacent slip. | |
| H1555-1555A | May 1911 | Queen's Road and shipyard men leaving work. TITANIC in background ready for launching. | |
| H1557 | May 1911 | Fitting starboard tail shaft prior to launch. | |
| H1558 | 31 May 1911 | Launch; port stern view entering water. | |
| H1559 | 31 May 1911 | Launch; port stern view entering water, fractionally sooner than above. | |
| H1560 | May 1911 | Port bow view on No. 3 slip in preparation for launch. | |
| H1561 | May 1911 | Port bow view on slip prior to launch. | |
| H1561A | May 1911 | As above, but plate cracked. | |
| H1566 | May 1911 | Hydraulic launch rams below port bow. | |
| H1568 | May 1911 | Port stern view on slip prior to launch. | |
| H1569 | 31 May 1911 | Port bow ¾ profile afloat immediately after launch. | |
| H1569A | 31 May 1911 | As above, but with slight differences in incidental details. | |
| H1637 | March 1912 | Starboard bow ¾ profile outfitting, with OLYMPIC (400) entering Thompson Graving Dock. | |
| H1656 | May 1911 | Distant view on No. 3 slip prior to launch, Thompson Graving Dock and poop deck of OLYMPIC in foreground. | |
| H1706 | March 1912 | Starboard bow view outfitting, with OLYMPIC entering Thompson Graving Dock. | |
| H1710 | c.May 1911 | Two main engines nearing completion in Engine Works erecting shop. | |
| H1711 | c.May 1911 | End view of port main engine nearing completion in Engine Works erecting shop. | |
| H1712 | c.September 1911 | Port bow ¾ profile at outfitting jetty, with funnels up, but unpainted. | |

| SHIP NO: 401 | | NAME: TITAN!C |
|---|---|---|
| REF. NO. | DATE | MAIN SUBJECT |
| H1713 | October 1911 | Port near profile during outfitting at Thompson deepwater wharf. |
| H1721 | 2 April 1912 | Starboard stern view of completed ship in Belfast Lough with accompanying tugs. |
| H1722 | 2 April 1912 | Port profile of completed ship in Belfast Lough with accompanying tugs. |
| H1723 | 2 April 1912 | Stern view as above. |
| H1724 | March 1912 | First class suite bedroom B57. |
| H1725 | March 1912 | First class suite bedroom B59. |
| H1726 | March 1912 | First class suite bedroom B60. |
| H1728 | March 1912 | First class suite bedroom B38. |
| H1729 | March 1912 | First class suite bedroom B64. |
| H1730 | March 1912 | First class gymnasium. |
| H1732 | March 1912 | First class suite bedroom B64. |
| H1733 | March 1912 | First class Cafe Parisienne on B deck. |
| H2372 | c.20 November 1909 | Port bow of OLYMPIC fully framed, with forward tank top of TITANIC on No. 3 slip. |
| H2377 | 6-15 April 1910 | Starboard bow view of TITANIC fully framed with OLYMPIC fully plated alongside. |
| H2378 | c.April 1910 | Starboard profile of builder's model without case, identified on the negative as OLYMPIC & TITANIC, but as OLYMPIC on the model. |
| H2379 | c.April 1910 | Starboard bow ¾ profile as above. |
| H2382 | 5 August 1910 | Port bow view of OLYMPIC on slip with TITANIC partially plated alongside (unsharp). |
| H2383 | c.April 1910 | Starboard bow ¾ profile of builder's half model OLYMPIC & TITANIC on adjustable base. |
| H2384 | c.April 1910 | Starboard stern ¾ profile of above. |
| H2385-2387 | c.April 1910 | Three views of builder's half model OLYMPIC/TITANIC, different to above. |
| H2401-2402 | c.April 1910 | Starboard near profile and profile of cased builder's model, OLYMPIC/TITANIC with sign 'the largest ships in the world.' |
| H2423 | c.October 1910 | General view of internal construction arrangement with gantry overhead. |

| SHIP NO: 403 | | NAME: LEICESTERSHIRE |
|---|---|---|
| TYPE: Passenger/Cargo Ship | TONNAGE: 8339 | LAUNCH: 3 June 1909 |
| DELIVERY: 11 September 1909 | | OWNER: Bibby Steamship Company |
| REF. NO. | DATE | MAIN SUBJECT |
| H1371 | June 1909 | Starboard bow ¾ profile on No. 9 slip, South Yard, prior to launch. |
| H1372 | June 1909 | Stern view on slip prior to launch. |
| H1373 | 3 June 1909 | Launch; stern view entering water. |
| H1374 | 3 June 1909 | Port bow view afloat in Abercorn Basin immediately after launch. View from bottom of slip. |

| SHIP NO: 404 | | NAME: KAROOLA |
|---|---|---|
| TYPE: Passenger Ship | TONNAGE: 7390 | LAUNCH: 9 March 1909 |
| DELIVERY: 8 July 1909 | | OWNER: McIlwraith McEachern & Company |
| REF. NO. | DATE | MAIN SUBJECT |
| H2299 | March 1909 | Starboard bow view on No. 1 slip, North Yard, prior to launch. |

| SHIP NO: 405 | | NAME: BERBICE |
|---|---|---|
| TYPE: | TONNAGE: | LAUNCH: |
| Passenger/Cargo Ship | 2379 | 6 May 1909 |
| DELIVERY: 8 July 1909 | | OWNER: Royal Mail Steam Packet Company |

| REF. NO. | DATE | MAIN SUBJECT |
|---|---|---|
| H1366 | 6 May 1909 | Launch; starboard stern view entering water from No. 8 slip, South Yard. |
| H1367 | 6 May 1909 | Port bow ¾ profile on slip prior to launch. |
| H1368 | 6 May 1909 | Port stern view on slip prior to launch. |
| H1369 | 6 May 1909 | Starboard bow ¾ profile afloat immediately after launch. |
| H1370 | July 1909 | Port stern ¾ profile of completed ship in Abercorn Basin. |
| H1375 | July 1909 | First class dining saloon. |
| H1376 | July 1909 | First class lounge/social hall, with wicker furniture. |
| H1377 | July 1909 | First class smoke room/alcove with wicker furniture. |

| SHIP NO: 406 | | NAME: BALANTIA |
|---|---|---|
| TYPE: | TONNAGE: | LAUNCH: |
| Passenger/Cargo Ship | 2379 | 28 October 1909 |
| DELIVERY: 18 December 1909 | | OWNER: Royal Mail Steam Packet Company |

| REF. NO. | DATE | MAIN SUBJECT |
|---|---|---|
| H1378 | 28 October 1909 | Port bow ¾ profile on No. 8 slip, South Yard, prior to launch. |
| H1379 | 28 October 1909 | Port stern ¾ profile on slip prior to launch. |
| H1380 | 28 October 1909 | Launch; view of starboard stern entering water. |
| H1381 | 28 October 1909 | Starboard bow ¾ profile afloat immediately after launch. |
| H1381A | 28 October 1909 | As above, but closer to bow view. |

| SHIP NO: 407 | | NAME: MALLINA |
|---|---|---|
| TYPE: | TONNAGE: | LAUNCH: |
| Cargo Ship | 3213 | 25 March 1909 |
| DELIVERY: 29 April 1909 | | OWNER: Australasian United Steam Navigation Company |

| REF. NO. | DATE | MAIN SUBJECT |
|---|---|---|
| H1362 | April 1909 | View aft from forecastle deck to bridge in final stage of outfitting, South Yard. |
| H1363 | April 1909 | View forward from bridge to forecastle deck in final stage of outfitting, South Yard. |
| H1364 | April 1909 | View aft from bridge to funnel and poop deck as above. |
| H1365 | April 1909 | View forward from poop deck to midship decks as above. |

| SHIP NO: 409 | | NAME: PAKEHA |
|---|---|---|
| TYPE: | TONNAGE: | LAUNCH: |
| Passenger/Cargo Ship | 7910 | 26 May 1910 |
| DELIVERY: 20 August 1910 | | OWNER: Shaw Savill & Albion Company |

| REF. NO. | DATE | MAIN SUBJECT |
|---|---|---|
| H2303 | c. August 1910 | Builder's half model, starboard side. |
| H2304 | May 1910 | Port stern ¾ profile on No. 5 slip, South Yard, prior to launch. |
| H2304A | May 1910 | Starboard bow view on slip prior to launch. |
| H2305 | 26 May 1910 | Launch; starboard stern view entering water. |
| H2305A | 26 May 1910 | Starboard stern ¾ profile afloat after launch. |

| SHIP NO: 410 | | NAME: EDINBURGH CASTLE |
|---|---|---|
| TYPE:<br>Passenger Ship | TONNAGE:<br>13326 | LAUNCH:<br>27 January 1910 |
| DELIVERY:<br>28 April 1910 | OWNER:<br>Union-Castle Mail Steamship Company | |

| REF. NO. | DATE | MAIN SUBJECT |
|---|---|---|
| H1382 | January 1910 | Starboard bow view on No. 1 slip, North Yard, prior to launch. |
| H1383 | January 1910 | Port stern view on slip prior to launch. |
| H1384 | 27 January 1910 | Launch party on platform and bottle breaking on port bow. |
| H1385 | 27 January 1910 | Port bow view alongside jetty after launch. |
| H1386 | April 1910 | Starboard near profile of completed ship in Belfast Lough. |
| H1387 | April 1910 | As above, but closer. |
| H2292 | January 1910 | Port stern view on slip prior to launch. |
| H2292A | 27 January 1910 | Launch; port stern view of hull entering water. |
| H2293 | April 1910 | First class dining saloon |
| H2293A | January 1910 | Elevated starboard view from adjoining gantry, prior to launch. |
| H2294 | April 1910 | First class lounge and well to dining saloon below. |
| H2294A | April 1910 | First class dining saloon with lounge well above. |
| H2295 | April 1910 | First class gentlemen's smoke room. |
| H2295A | April 1910 | First class library, reading and writing room. |
| H2296 | April 1910 | First class smoking lounge with staircase. |
| H2296A | April 1910 | Second class smoke room. |
| H2297 | April 1910 | Second class dining saloon. |
| H2297A | April 1910 | First class entrance hall and staircase. |
| H2298 | April 1910 | Second class library. |

| SHIP NO: 411 | | NAME: GLOUCESTERSHIRE |
|---|---|---|
| TYPE:<br>Passenger/Cargo Ship | TONNAGE:<br>8324 | LAUNCH:<br>7 July 1910 |
| DELIVERY:<br>22 October 1910 | OWNER:<br>Bibby Steamship Company | |

| REF. NO. | DATE | MAIN SUBJECT |
|---|---|---|
| H1388 | July 1910 | Port bow view on No. 6 slip, South Yard, prior to launch. |
| H1389 | July 1910 | Starboard stern view on slip prior to launch. |
| H1390 | 7 July 1910 | Launch; view of starboard side of hull entering water. |
| H1391-1391A | 7 July 1910 | Starboard bow view off Queen's Quay in Victoria Channel, after launch. |

| SHIP NO: 412 | | NAME: THEMISTOCLES |
|---|---|---|
| **TYPE:** | **TONNAGE:** | **LAUNCH:** |
| Passenger/Cargo Ship | 11231 | 22 September 1910 |
| **DELIVERY:** | | **OWNER:** |
| 12 January 1911 | | George Thompson & Company |

| REF. NO. | DATE | MAIN SUBJECT |
|---|---|---|
| H1392 | September 1910 | Port stern view on No. 7 slip, South Yard, prior to launch. |
| H1393 | September 1910 | Starboard bow view on slip prior to launch. |
| H1394 | 22 September 1910 | Launch party on platform and bottle breaking on port bow. |
| H1395 | 22 September 1910 | Starboard bow view alongside No. 1 outfitting jetty, after launch. |
| H1396 | January 1911 | View forward along starboard boat deck. |
| H1397 | January 1911 | View forward from starboard side of poop deck. |
| H1398 | January 1911 | First class verandah smoke room. |
| H1399 | January 1911 | Starboard near profile, nearing completion at No. 1 outfitting jetty. |
| H1400 | January 1911 | Starboard bow view, nearing completion at outfitting jetty. |
| H1401 | January 1911 | First class cabin. |
| H1402 | January 1911 | Third class single berth cabin. |
| H1403 | January 1911 | Third class smoke room/general room. |
| H1404 | January 1911 | First class smoke room. |
| H1405 | January 1911 | First class stateroom, sitting and writing room. |
| H1406 | January 1911 | First class lounge/writing and reading room. |
| H1407 | January 1911 | Third class smoke room/general room. |
| H2335A | January 1911 | Starboard bow ¾ profile of builder's model, without case. |
| H2335B | January 1911 | Starboard profile of builder's model, without case. |

| SHIP NO: 413 | | NAME: SACHSEN |
|---|---|---|
| **TYPE:** | **TONNAGE:** | **LAUNCH:** |
| Passenger/Cargo Ship | 7986 | 17 November 1910 |
| **DELIVERY:** | | **OWNER:** |
| 21 January 1911 | | Hamburg-Amerika Line |

| REF. NO. | DATE | MAIN SUBJECT |
|---|---|---|
| H2334 | November 1908 | Starboard bow ¾ profile on No. 9 slip, South Yard prior to launch. |
| H2334A | November 1908 | Starboard stern view on slip prior to launch. |

| SHIP NO: 414 | | NAME: MALOJA |
|---|---|---|
| **TYPE:** | **TONNAGE:** | **LAUNCH:** |
| Passenger Ship | 12430 | 17 December 1910 |
| **DELIVERY:** | | **OWNER:** |
| 7 September 1911 | | Peninsular and Oriental Steam Navigation Company |

| REF. NO. | DATE | MAIN SUBJECT |
|---|---|---|
| H1642 | September 1911 | First class dining saloon. |
| H1643 | September 1911 | First class smoke room. |
| H1644 | September 1911 | First class reading and writing room, with dome panels, central well and dining saloon below. |
| H1645 | September 1911 | First class cabin. |
| H1646 | September 1911 | Second class dining saloon. |
| H1647 | September 1911 | Second class smoke room. |
| H1648 | September 1911 | Second class reading and writing room. |
| H2326 | September 1911 | Starboard profile of builder's model, without case. |
| H2327 | December 1910 | Starboard bow view on No. 1 slip, North Yard, prior to launch. |
| H2328 | December 1910 | Port stern view on slip, prior to launch. |

| SHIP NO: 415 | | NAME: ARLANZA |
|---|---|---|

| TYPE: | TONNAGE: | LAUNCH: |
|---|---|---|
| Passenger Ship | 15043 | 23 November 1911 |

| DELIVERY: | OWNER: |
|---|---|
| 8 June 1912 | Royal Mail Steam Packet Company |

| REF. NO. | DATE | MAIN SUBJECT |
|---|---|---|
| H1649 | November 1911 | Port bow ¾ profile on No. 2 slip, North Yard, prior to launch. |
| H1650 | November 1911 | Port stern view on slip prior to launch. |
| H1651 | 23 November 1911 | Launch; port stern view entering water. |
| H1652 | 23 November 1911 | Port bow view afloat immediately after launch. |
| H1738 | June 1912 | Port stern view of completed ship in Belfast Lough. |
| H1739-1739A | June 1912 | First class social hall. |
| H1740 | June 1912 | First class upper smoke room. |
| H1741-1742 | June 1912 | First class dining saloon. |
| H1743 | June 1912 | Verandah of first class smoke room. |
| H1744-1745 | June 1912 | First class entrance hall and main staircase on D deck. |
| H1746 | June 1912 | Sitting room of first class cabine de luxe. |
| H1747 | June 1912 | View aft along port deck towards funnel. |
| H1748 | June 1912 | View aft along starboard first class promenade deck. |
| H1749 | June 1912 | Second class smoke room with mast passing through floor to ceiling. |
| H1750 | June 1912 | Second class social hall/reading and writing room, with mast passing through floor to ceiling. |
| H1751 | June 1912 | Second class dining saloon. |
| H1752 | June 1912 | Second class entrance from port lower promenade deck. |
| H1753 | June 1912 | Sitting room of first class No. 1 suite. |
| H1754 | June 1912 | Bedroom of first class No. 1 suite. |
| H1755 | June 1912 | Bedroom of first class No. 2 suite. |
| H1756 | June 1912 | Sitting room of first class No. 2 suite. |
| H1757 | June 1912 | First class state room No. 5. |
| H1758 | June 1912 | First class cabin No. 660. |
| H1759 | June 1912 | First class 'bibby' cabin. |
| H1760 | June 1912 | First class double cabin, No. 239 B deck. |
| H1761 | June 1912 | Bedroom of first class suite. |
| H1761A | June 1912 | Port bow view of completed ship in Thompson Graving Dock. |

| SHIP NO: 418 | | NAME: DEMOSTHENES |
|---|---|---|

| TYPE: | TONNAGE: | LAUNCH: |
|---|---|---|
| Passenger/Cargo Ship | 11223 | 28 February 1911 |

| DELIVERY: | OWNER: |
|---|---|
| 5 August 1911 | George Thompson & Company |

| REF. NO. | DATE | MAIN SUBJECT |
|---|---|---|
| H1408 | 28 February 1911 | Starboard bow view on No. 5 slip, South Yard, prior to launch. |
| H1409 | 28 February 1911 | Port stern view on slip showing triple screw arrangement. |
| H1410 | 28 February 1911 | Starboard bow view on slip, with launch party on platform. |
| H1411 | 28 February 1911 | Port bow view afloat immediately after launch. |
| H2322 | c. August 1911 | Starboard bow ¾ profile of cased builder's model. |
| H2324 | c. August 1911 | Starboard profile of cased builder's model. |
| H2324A | 28 February 1911 | Launch; starboard stern view entering water. |

| SHIP NO: 419 | | NAME: GALWAY CASTLE |
|---|---|---|

| TYPE: | TONNAGE: | LAUNCH: |
|---|---|---|
| Passenger Ship | 7987 | 12 April 1911 |

| DELIVERY: | OWNER: |
|---|---|
| 9 October 1911 | Union-Castle Mail Steamship Company |

| REF. NO. | DATE | MAIN SUBJECT |
|---|---|---|
| H1551 | April 1911 | Port bow view on No. 6 slip, South Yard, prior to launch. |
| H1552 | April 1911 | Starboard stern ¾ profile on slip prior to launch. |
| H1553 | 12 April 1911 | Launch; starboard stern view entering water. |
| H1554 | 12 April 1911 | Port bow ¾ profile afloat after launch. |

| SHIP NO: 420 | | NAME: DESEADO |
|---|---|---|
| **TYPE:** Passenger Ship | **TONNAGE:** 11471 | **LAUNCH:** 26 October 1911 |
| **DELIVERY:** 27 June 1912 | **OWNER:** Royal Mail Steam Packet Company | |

| REF. NO. | DATE | MAIN SUBJECT |
|---|---|---|
| H1697 | October 1911 | Starboard bow ¾ profile on No. 9 slip, South Yard, prior to launch. |
| H1698 | October 1911 | Starboard stern view on slip prior to launch. |
| H1699 | 26 October 1911 | Launch; starboard stern view entering water. |
| H1700 | 26 October 1911 | Starboard bow view afloat immediately after launch. |
| H1766 | June 1912 | Port bow ¾ profile of completed ship in Belfast Lough. |
| H1767 | June 1912 | View forward along port boat deck towards funnel. |
| H1768 | June 1912 | View aft along starboard promenade deck. |
| H1769 | June 1912 | First class social hall. |
| H1771 | June 1912 | First class smoke room. |
| H1772 | June 1912 | Verandah of first class smoke room, with posed figures. |
| H2325 | June 1912 | Starboard profile of cased builder's model. |

| SHIP NO: 421 | | NAME: ZEALANDIC |
|---|---|---|
| **TYPE:** Passenger/Cargo Ship | **TONNAGE:** 10897 | **LAUNCH:** 29 June 1911 |
| **DELIVERY:** 12 October 1911 | **OWNER:** Oceanic Steam Navigation Company (White Star Line) | |

| REF. NO. | DATE | MAIN SUBJECT |
|---|---|---|
| H1638 | 29 June 1911 | Starboard bow view on No. 7 slip, South Yard, prior to launch. |
| H1639 | 29 June 1911 | Starboard stern view on slip prior to launch. |
| H1640 | 29 June 1911 | Launch; starboard stern view entering water. |

| SHIP NO: 422 | | NAME: NOMADIC |
|---|---|---|
| **TYPE:** Passenger Ship Tender | **TONNAGE:** 1260 | **LAUNCH:** 25 April 1911 |
| **DELIVERY:** 27 May 1911 | **OWNER:** Oceanic Steam Navigation Company (White Star Line) | |

| REF. NO. | DATE | MAIN SUBJECT |
|---|---|---|
| H2329 | April 1911 | Bow view on No. 1 slip, North Yard, prior to launch. |
| H2330 | 25 April 1911 | Port stern ¾ profile afloat after launch. |

| SHIP NO: 424 | | NAME: PATRIOTIC |
|---|---|---|
| **TYPE:** Passenger Ship | **TONNAGE:** 2254 | **LAUNCH:** 7 September 1911 |
| **DELIVERY:** 28 March 1912 | **OWNER:** Belfast Steamship Company | |

| REF. NO. | DATE | MAIN SUBJECT |
|---|---|---|
| H1412 | September 1911 | Starboard bow view on No. 1 slip, North Yard, prior to launch. |
| H1413 | September 1911 | View of port stern, propellers and rudder on slip prior to launch. |
| H1414 | September 1911 | Distant view of stern from lower end of slip, prior to launch. |
| H1415 | 7 September 1911 | Launch; port stern view entering water. |

| SHIP NO: 427 | NAME: DARRO | |
|---|---|---|
| TYPE:<br>Passenger Ship | TONNAGE:<br>11484 | LAUNCH:<br>16 May 1912 |
| DELIVERY:<br>31 October 1912 | OWNER:<br>Royal Mail Steam Packet Company | |

| REF. NO. | DATE | MAIN SUBJECT |
|---|---|---|
| H1734 | May 1912 | Port bow view on No. 6 slip, South Yard, prior to launch. |
| H1735 | May 1912 | Starboard stern view on slip prior to launch. |
| H1736 | 16 May 1912 | Launch; starboard stern view entering water. |
| H1737 | 16 May 1912 | Port stern ¾ profile afloat in Victoria Channel immediately after launch. |
| H1737A | 16 May 1912 | Starboard bow ¾ profile after launch, with Abercorn Basin and Coal Quay in foreground. |

| SHIP NO: 429 | NAME: OXFORDSHIRE | |
|---|---|---|
| TYPE:<br>Passenger/Cargo Ship | TONNAGE:<br>8623 | LAUNCH:<br>15 June 1912 |
| DELIVERY:<br>17 September 1912 | OWNER:<br>Bibby Steamship Company | |

| REF. NO. | DATE | MAIN SUBJECT |
|---|---|---|
| H1417 | September 1912 | Starboard profile of completed ship at outfitting jetty in Abercorn Basin. |
| H1657 | June 1912 | Engine beds and crankshafts in Engine Works erecting shop. |
| H1801 | c.June 1912 | Boilers under construction in Engine Works boiler shop. |

| SHIP NO: 430 | NAME: ABOSSO | |
|---|---|---|
| TYPE:<br>Passenger/Cargo Ship | TONNAGE:<br>7782 | LAUNCH:<br>15 August 1912 |
| DELIVERY:<br>19 December 1912 | OWNER:<br>African Steamship Company (Elder Dempster group) | |

| REF. NO. | DATE | MAIN SUBJECT |
|---|---|---|
| H1778 | 15 August 1912 | Starboard stern view on No. 9 slip, South Yard, prior to launch. |
| H1779 | 15 August 1912 | Launch; starboard stern view entering water. |
| H1780 | 15 August 1912 | Starboard stern view coming alongside No. 1 outfitting jetty after launch. |
| H1781 | December 1912 | Starboard bow view of almost completed ship alongside outfitting jetty. |
| H1782 | December 1912 | First class dining saloon. |
| H1783 | December 1912 | First class smoke room. |
| H1784-1785 | December 1912 | First class lounge. |
| H1786 | December 1912 | Second class dining saloon. |
| H1787 | December 1912 | Second class reading and writing room. |
| H1788 | December 1912 | First class gymnasium. |
| H1789 | December 1912 | Second class four berth cabin B47. |
| H1795 | December 1912 | First class two berth cabin B23. |
| H1796 | December 1912 | First class two berth cabin. |
| H1797 | December 1912 | First class stateroom B15. |
| H1798 | December 1912 | First class single cot cabin B6, with camera reflected in wardrobe mirror. |
| H1799 | December 1912 | View aft over boat deck from port bridge wing while at sea. |
| H1800 | December 1912 | Starboard near profile of completed ship in Belfast Lough. |

# REPAIR AND REFITTING OF SHIPS NOT BUILT BY H&W

| REF. NO. | DATE | SHIP | MAIN SUBJECT |
|---|---|---|---|
| H47 | Probably 1905 | SCOT renamed OCEANA | General view of first class dining saloon. |
| H48 | Probably 1905 | SCOT renamed OCEANA | Side view of first class dining saloon. |
| H49 | Probably 1905 | SCOT renamed OCEANA | General view of first class music saloon. |
| H50 | Probably 1905 | SCOT renamed OCEANA | Corner of first class music saloon. |
| H51 | 1905 | OCEANA ex SCOT | Port profile on completion of refitting as cruise liner for Hamburg-Amerika Line. |
| H52 | 1897 | AUGUSTA VICTORIA | Bow view in Alexandra Graving Dock prior to hull lengthening. |
| H53 | 1897 | AUGUSTA VICTORIA | Bow view from floor of dock showing cradle and gear for separating hull. |
| H54 | 1897 | AUGUSTA VICTORIA | Starboard bow view from side of dock showing cradle and gear. |
| H55 | 1897 | AUGUSTA VICTORIA | Midships view with rivets removed from shell plating. |
| H66 | 1897 | AUGUSTA VICTORIA | Bow view during hull lengthening. |
| H67 | 1897 | AUGUSTA VICTORIA | Inserted hull floors with cross-section of separated forward hull. |
| H68 | 1897 | AUGUSTA VICTORIA | Inserted hull floors with cross-section of separated after hull. |
| H69 | 1897 | AUGUSTA VICTORIA | Profile view from dock side of separated hulls. |
| H69A | 1897 | AUGUSTA VICTORIA | View as above, with newly constructed hull insertion. |
| H69B | 1897 | AUGUSTA VICTORIA | View as above, but on port side. |
| H460 | March 1900 | PARIS, renamed PHILADELPHIA | Alongside Alexandra Wharf with 100 ton crane removing machinery. |
| H461 | March 1900 | PARIS, renamed PHILADELPHIA | View of above, from south side of Alexandra Graving Dock. |
| H462 | March 1900 | PARIS, renamed PHILADELPHIA | Starboard stern view in Alexandra Graving Dock for hull repairs and refitting. |
| H463 | March 1900 | PARIS, renamed PHILADELPHIA | Port bow view as above. |
| H464 | March 1900 | PARIS, renamed PHILADELPHIA | Bow view from dock floor. |
| H465 | March 1900 | PARIS, renamed PHILADELPHIA | Port side view in dry dock from slightly elevated position. |
| H466-469 | March 1900 | PARIS, renamed PHILADELPHIA | Views from dockside, showing arrangement of supporting timber shores. |
| H470-471 | March 1900 | PARIS, renamed PHILADELPHIA | Views of damaged underside hull and supporting shores, from dock floor. |
| H472-477 | April 1900 | PARIS, renamed PHILADELPHIA | Views of damaged bottom plates and temporary repairs. |
| H478 | April 1900 | PARIS, renamed PHILADELPHIA | Stern view with stern frames and plates removed. |
| H479 | April 1900 | PARIS, renamed PHILADELPHIA | Engine room from dock floor with machinery and double bottom removed. |
| H480 | April 1900 | PARIS, renamed PHILADELPHIA | Underside of hull with damaged plates removed. |
| H481 | April 1900 | PARIS, renamed PHILADELPHIA | Stern view with stern frames and plates removed, renamed PHILADELPHIA. |
| H482-484 | October 1900 | PARIS, renamed PHILADELPHIA | Engine room with machinery and double bottom removed, repairs beginning. |
| H485-487 | October 1900 | PARIS, renamed PHILADELPHIA | Views of underside of hull from dock floor with plates and frames removed. |
| H488 | August 1901 | PHILADELPHIA | Port bow ¾ profile at sea after repairs and refitting. |
| H489 | c.1901 | PHILADELPHIA | Stern view with replacement stern post and stern frames. |
| H490 | c.1901 | PHILADELPHIA | Side view with frames and plates removed. |
| H491 | c.1901 | PHILADELPHIA | Stern view, with tarpaulins shrouding stern post. |
| H492 | c.1901 | PHILADELPHIA | Bottom view with frames and plates removed. |
| H493 | c.1901 | PHILADELPHIA | Engine room with double bottom in course of replacement. |
| H494 | c.1901 | PHILADELPHIA | Replacement of bottom frames and plates. |
| H495 | c.1901 | PHILADELPHIA | Engine room with floor plates in course of replacement. |
| H496 | c.1901 | PHILADELPHIA | Replacement of bow frames and plates, portside. |
| H497 | c.1901 | PHILADELPHIA | Deck view forward during refitting in dry dock. |

| REF. NO. | DATE | SHIP | MAIN SUBJECT |
|---|---|---|---|
| H498 | c.1901 | PHILADELPHIA | Deck view aft during refitting in dry dock. |
| H499 | c.1901 | PHILADELPHIA | Port stern view in dry dock with plating completed and propellers fitted. |
| H701 | c.1901 | PHILADELPHIA | Stern view from floor of dry dock showing propellers repaired and underside of hull. |
| H702 | c.1901 | PHILADELPHIA | Port bow view from floor of dry dock, hull repairs completed. |
| H703 | c.1901 | PHILADELPHIA | Port bow view from side of dry dock, hull repairs completed. |
| H704 | c.1901 | PHILADELPHIA | Starboard bow ¾ profile, hull not repainted, moored off Alexandra Wharf. |
| H705 | c.1901 | PHILADELPHIA | Starboard stern ¾ profile as above. |
| H706 | c.1901 | PHILADELPHIA | Port bow ¾ profile, refitting completed, steaming in Belfast Lough. |
| H707 | 1901 | PHILADELPHIA | Port stern ¾ profile, refitting completed, steaming in Belfast Lough. |
| H707A | 1901 | PHILADELPHIA | Starboard profile, refitting completed, steaming in Belfast Lough. |
| H725 | c.1902 | EUROPA | Starboard bow ¾ profile of single screw cargo ship in Hamilton Graving Dock. |
| H726 | c.1902 | EUROPA | Starboard stern view as above. |
| H728 | 1902 | HMS HERMES | Starboard bow ¾ profile of cruiser alongside Alexandra Wharf for reboilering. |
| H729 | 1902 | HMS HERMES | Port bow view ¾ profile of cruiser alongside Alexandra Wharf for reboilering. |

| REF. NO. | DATE | SHIP | MAIN SUBJECT |
|---|---|---|---|
| H831 | | NEW YORK | Bow view in Alexandra Graving Dock with damaged clipper stem. |
| H832 | | NEW YORK | Starboard bow view as above. |
| H833 | | NEW YORK | Port bow view as above. |
| H834-834A | | NEW YORK | View of buckled plates on underside hull and temporary repairs, from floor of the dock. |
| H1692-1693 | 1905 | ORTONA renamed ARCADIAN | First class smoke room, pre-refitting. |
| H1694 | 1905 | ORTONA renamed ARCADIAN | First class dining saloon, pre-refitting. |
| H1695 | 1905 | ORTONA renamed ARCADIAN | First class reading and writing room, pre-refitting. |
| H1696 | 1905 | ORTONA renamed ARCADIAN | Starboard bow ¾ profile, refitting at No. 1 Jetty, South Yard. |
| H1701 | 1905 | ARCADIAN | Port profile at sea after refitting for Royal Mail Line. |
| H1702 | 1905 | ARCADIAN | Port bow ¾ profile as above, with stern of tug in foreground. |
| H1716-1717 | 1905 | ARCADIAN | First class dining saloon after refitting. |
| H1718 | 1905 | ARCADIAN | First class smoke room after refitting. |
| H1719 | 1905 | ARCADIAN | First class reading and writing room after refitting. |
| H2307-2318 | March 1896 | SCOT | Sequence of views of ship in Alexandra Graving Dock, showing operation to lengthen hull by 54 feet. |
| H2319 | March 1896 | SCOT | Panelling in first class dining saloon. |
| H2320 | March 1896 | SCOT | Panelling and side seating in first class music room. |

# OFFICES, WORKSHOPS, PLANT AND FACILITIES

| REF. NO. | DATE | MAIN SUBJECT |
|---|---|---|
| H1–17 | 1 October 1896 – 1 March 1897 | Reconstruction of No. 8 slip, renumbered 2, North Yard for building OCEANIC (317). |
| H56 | June 1912 | New platers shed (north), with machinery, crane and platers. |
| H57 | c.1910 | Mould loft with three loftsmen chalking ship's lines on floor. |
| H58 | June 1912 | New foundry, with moulds, castings and foundrymen. |
| H59 | June 1912 | Old and new sections of foundry, with moulds, castings and foundrymen. |
| H74 | c.January 1897 | Atmospheric, snow-covered view of North Yard from bridge of PENNSYLVANIA (302). |
| H94 | c.1898 | Engine Works erecting shop with machinery components for OCEANIC (317). |
| H96 | c.1901 | Engine Works erecting shop with machinery components for MINNETONKA (339). |
| H97–H98 | June 1912 | Engine Works turning shop with machinery components for CERAMIC (432). |
| H99 | c.1900 | Engine Works small tools and brass shop. |
| H100 | June 1912 | Engine Works brass finishing shop. |
| H242, 242A, 243 | c. August 1899 | Office display of half models of White Star liners OCEANIC (73), MAJESTIC (209) and OCEANIC (317). |
| H244–244A | c.1899 | Office display of five half models of unidentified White Star cargo liners. |
| H355B–355C | November 1898 | View of South Yard and Engine Works across Abercorn Basin from south. |
| H355D | December 1898 | View of South Yard, including outfitting jetties across Abercorn Basin from south east. |
| H396B | November 1901 | Painting of unidentified Union liner at Cowes, landing Lord Roberts. |
| H500 | c.1912 | Front of new three storey main offices, Queen's Road. |
| H501 | c.1912 | Hull drawing office with naval architects. |
| H502 | c.1912 | Front of new three storey extended main offices, Queen's Road. |
| H503 | c.1912 | Office of chairman, Lord Pirrie. |
| H504 | c.1912 | Consultation room, with paintings of OCEANIC (317) and PHILADELPHIA ex PARIS. |
| H505 | 1899 | Painters' studio and painters. |
| H506 | 1899 | Painters' shop interior with painters and barrels of paint. |
| H507 | 1899 | Rigging shed interior. |
| H508 | 1899 | Spar makers' shed interior. |
| H509 | 1899 | Sail loft, with Belfast truss roof, interior. |
| H510 | 1899 | Upholsterers' shop interior. |
| H511 | 1899 | Photographic studio darkroom. |
| H512 | 1899 | Boatbuilders' shed, with planked-up clinker lifeboats, interior. |
| H513–515 | 1899 | Timber stores exterior. |
| H516 | 1899 | Hydraulic engine house interior. |
| H517 | 1899 | Hydraulic accumulators, exterior. |
| H518 | 1899 | Hydraulic accumulator, North Yard. |
| H519 | c.1899 | Gantry over No. 8 slip, renumbered 2, North Yard. |
| H520 | November 1909 | Arrol gantry with OLYMPIC (400) in frame on No. 2 slip, north side view. |
| H522 | c.1899 | Alexandra repair shops from Queen's Road. |
| H523 | c.1899 | Boiler shop exterior. |
| H524 | c.1899 | Engine works erecting shop from Abercorn Basin. |
| H525 | c.1899 | General view of engine works exterior (cracked and broken plate). |
| H526 | c.1899 | Pattern shop exterior. |
| H527 | c.1899 | Iron foundry exterior. |
| H528 | c.1899 | Smiths' shop/forge exterior. |
| H529 | c.1899 | General view of stock piled plates and fitting plates north shed, North Yard. |
| H530 | c.1899 | General view, north iron shed, North Yard. |
| H531 | c.1899 | West iron platers' shed, North Yard. |
| H532 | c.1899 | East iron platers' shed, North Yard. |
| H533 | c.1899 | Joiners' shop/sawmill from Queen's Road. |
| H534 | c.1899 | Plumbers' shop and mould loft exterior. |
| H535 | c.1899 | Elevated view of South and North Yards and Hamilton Graving Dock, with 3 masted barque. |
| H536 | c.1899 | Iron foundry exterior. |
| H537 | c.1899 | Saw-dust conveyor, boiler house interior. |
| H538 | c.1899 | Mast house interior, with riveted steel masts. |
| H539 | c.1899 | Polish ship interior with polishers. |
| H540 | c.1899 | Ship carpenters' shop (plug making), interior. |
| H541 | c.1899 | Sawmill new bay interior. |
| H542 | c.1899 | Sawmill interior. |
| H543 | c.1899 | Plumbers' shop interior from south end. |
| H544 | c.1899 | Plumbers' shop interior from north end. |
| H545–46 | c.1899 | Cabinet shop interior. |
| H547 | c.1899 | Shipyard main store interior. |
| H548 | c.1899 | Rivets store interior. |
| H549 | c.1899 | Joiners' work store interior, with stored furniture. |

| REF. NO. | DATE | MAIN SUBJECT |
|---|---|---|
| H647 | 1908 | Iron shipwrights' shop interior, Southampton. |
| H648 | 1908 | Boiler shop interior, Southampton. |
| H649 | 1908 | Sailmakers' loft, Southampton. |
| H650 | June 1912 | Generating station interior. |
| H730–731 | August 1901 | Office display of half models of White Star ships CUFIC/RUNIC (210 & 211), CEVIC (270) and CELTIC (335). |
| H980 | c.June 1906 | Elevated view of North Yard from B crane with ADRIATIC (358) under construction on No. 3 slip. |
| H1220–1250 | 1907–1908 | Reconstruction of North Yard slips 2–4 to form new slips 2–3, and erection of Arrol gantry for building OLYMPIC (400) and TITANIC (401). |
| H1323–1326 | c.December 1908 | Arrol gantry and progress on reconstruction of slips 2–3, including laid keel of OLYMPIC (400) on No. 2 slip. |
| H1335 | c.1909 | Piping and plant in generating station. |
| H1555–1555A | May 1911 | Queen's Road with shipyard men leaving work. TITANIC in background ready for launching. |
| H1656 | May 1911 | General view aft from OLYMPIC, showing Thompson Graving Dock and TITANIC on slip in background. |
| H1657 | June 1912 | Engine Works erecting shop, with machinery for Ship Nos. 429 and 432. |
| H1658 | c.June 1912 | Engine Works new turbine erecting shop, with machinery for Ship Nos. 433 and 436. |
| H1658A | c.June 1912 | Engine Works new turbine erecting shop. |
| H1659 | c.June 1912 | Engine Works new valve shop. |
| H1660 | c.June 1912 | Engine Works new turbine erecting shop. |
| H1661 | c.June 1912 | Iron foundry, interior. |
| H1801 | c.June 1912 | Engine Works boiler shop with scrapping machine and boilers for Ship No. 429. |
| H1802 | c.June 1912 | Engine Works boiler shop with drilling machine and furnace for Ship No. 433. |
| H1805 | c.June 1912 | Engine Works turning shop. |
| H1806–1807 | c.1912 | Erection of Sulzer diesel engine in generating station. |
| H2355 | c.1905 | Port profile of ex-Admiralty screw tug JACKAL, which replaced paddle tug DESPATCH. |
| H2473–2514 | May 1906 — Oct 1908 | Sequence showing erection and testing of 200 ton floating crane. |
| H2517–2517A | c.1908 | Two views of main offices, Queen's Road. |
| H2518–2549 | c.Feb 1908 — 14 April 1908 | Sequence showing erection of Arrol gantry over North Yard slip Nos. 2 & 3. |
| H2550–2567 | Nov 1908 — Jan 1909 | Sequence showing 200 ton floating crane working. |
| H2568–2617 | April 1908 — 15 August 1909 | Sequence showing erection of Arrol gantry over North Yard slip Nos. 2 & 3. |

*R J Welch, Harland & Wolff's official photographer, recording the drydocking of TITANIC's sistership OLYMPIC (400), 1 April 1911. Photograph (detail) by W A Green (UFTM/WAG 3196).*